WORLDS
WITHOUT
END

WORLDS
WITHOUT
END

A Reflection on Planets,

Life, and Time

by N. J. BERRILL

The Macmillan Company, New York
Collier-Macmillan Limited, London

First Printing

The Macmillan Company, New York
Collier-Macmillan Canada Ltd., Toronto, Ontario

Library of Congress catalog card number: 64–24307

DESIGNED BY MARY A. BROWN

Printed in the United States of America

ACKNOWLEDGMENTS

THE AUTHOR WISHES TO THANK the following for their kind permission to quote from previously copyrighted material:

American Institute of Physics for passages from "Wiggleworm
Physics" by Dr. Jerome Rothstein, which appeared in the Sep-
tember 1962 issue of *Physics Today.*

Harcourt, Brace & World, Inc., for quotations from *Tales of
Ten Worlds* by Arthur C. Clarke © 1961 by Ziff-Davis Publishing
Company. Reprinted from *Tales of Ten Worlds* by Arthur C.
Clarke by permission of Harcourt, Brace & World, Inc.

Harper & Row, Publishers, Incorporated, for passages from
The Silent World by J. Y. Cousteau with Frederic Dumas (Harper & Brothers, 1953).

Harvard University Press for passages from "The Termitodoxa" by William Wheeler, which appeared in *Essays in Philo-
sophical Biology,* issued in 1939.

Science for passages from "The General Limits of Space
Travel" by Dr. Sebastian von Hoerner in the July 6, 1962, issue,
pages 19, 21 and 22. Copyright 1962 by the American Association
for the Advancement of Science.

Mr. Ernest Tricomi for permission to quote his letter to *Time*
which appeared in the March 22, 1963 issue.

Preface

Ever since the invention of the telescope some three hundred years ago we have been speculating concerning the nature of inhabitants of planets other than the Earth. Now space rockets and satellites are leading the way to interplanetary travel. Cosmic theories, moreover, now postulate the presence of planetary systems associated with a large percentage of stars in the galaxy, and life-bearing planets may well exist by the million. Most biologists are convinced that in any solar system a well placed and well founded planet will inevitably give rise to a life of its own that is as diverse as that of the Earth. Whether or not we ourselves will ever be able to reach such planets is less significant than obtaining some understanding of what sort of life may be present on them.

The Earth and Earthly life must necessarily be our yardstick, for there is no other, and we can proceed speculatively only from the known into the unknown. Beyond a certain stage, however, the imagination fails, for we are at a loss to conjure up the completely strange. In this book, therefore, I have attempted to explore the vast but vague subject of exobiology, which means the study of life way out there, and in several ways—by comparing our nearest and best known planets with the Earth, by examining hypothetical planets not unlike the Earth but with one or another feature altered in some manner, so as to see how familiar living things would have been affected, by examining the life of the Earth to see what characteristics may be regarded as universal under certain circumstances and what are special, and by presenting the imaginative efforts of various speculative writers to conceive and describe creatures different from those known to us here. Altogether, this account of the possibilities of life on other planets is inevitably impressionistic. It is also, in a back-of-the-mirror sort of way, a reflection of the nature of man and of his own world. As a study of worlds without end, however, it concerns life, time, and space, each in full measure.

Contents

	PREFACE	*v*
1	VENUS OBSERVED	*1*
2	MOONSTRUCK	*14*
3	OUTWARD BOUND	*32*
4	MARTIAN LANDING	*49*
5	OUT FROM THE SUN	*63*
6	OUT OF THEIR MINDS	*80*
7	GRAVITY GETS YOU DOWN	*91*
8	WATER, WATER, EVERYWHERE	*106*
9	GREAT EXPECTATIONS	*120*
10	LANDED GENTRY	*139*
11	IS SEX NECESSARY?	*150*
12	QUESTIONS OF TIME	*163*

13   SINGLES AND DOUBLES   178

14   TALKING TO THE NATIVES   193

15   POINT OF NO RETURN   208

16   EARTH AS A SPACE SHIP   222

     FURTHER READING   233

     INDEX   235

WORLDS
WITHOUT
END

O N E

Venus Observed

FROM TIME IMMEMORIAL man has been looking skyward for
inspiration, sudden death, and salvation. Angels from
heaven, flying saucers from who knows where, satellites and
planetary probes of our own creation have had their turn.
All great gods have had their seats on high. Worship of the
sun and the moon led to the old priests' theory of accord
between heavenly and earthly events. Their orderly behavior was extended to the planets, and the gods of the
Pantheon were Jupiter, Venus, Saturn, Mercury and Mars.

Now Venus, Goddess of Beauty and star of the morning
and evening, with the connivance of the Jet Propulsion
Laboratory, has been shot at and dethroned. Mariner II,*
passing close by on a sunward probe, sensitive to all forms
of radiation and cosmic pulls but unaware of the adoration

---

* Forward-sounding names have been assigned to the various series of
space probes. Explorers and Vanguards have been Earth-orbiting satellites.
The Ranger series were unsuccessful Moon probes. Mariner I, weighing
more than 1,000 pounds and destined for Venus, could not be supplied on
time with the necessary thrust. Mariner II, less than half that weight, was
a stripped-down version that could be sent on its way by available rockets.

and hopes of men, reported that the veil of Venus covered a smooth, hard surface as hot as melted lead, and consisted of deadly hydrocarbons, without sign of oxygen or water. And no magnetic field.

No field, no spin. No water, no life. The Earth's twin sister has been stillborn from the start, or so it seems. So, somewhat downcast by this conclusion, we turn our thoughts of space outward toward the colder night, realists that we are. Yet the wistful hope still lingers here and there, and as long as no one has actually peered beneath the dense cloud cover of Venus, the planet may cling to life at least in our imagination.

When judgment is made, what is the measure? Can we judge another by ourself, whether man or planet? We know the Earth to be good for life. Must all that is different be worse? One retort to the Mariner's verdict came ostensibly from Venus itself in the form of a letter published in an Earthly magazine with global circulation, which shows ourself as others might see us. Here it is in full:

"A few months ago, Venusian scientists launched a compact bundle of sophisticated space instruments called Earth Explorer II into an orbit that approached Earth within 21,000 miles. Following is the report of the Jupiter-Pluto Laboratories, known as JPL, which was the Government agency responsible for the exploration:

"Earth appears to be a dead and decaying planet, quite incapable of supporting any kind of life.

"Our telemetry equipment reported back to us that Earth is surrounded by a hostile atmosphere which is stabilized to a remarkable degree. Even in the upper atmosphere, winds do not attain a speed greater than about 200 m.p.h., while at the surface the winds appear to move at from 5 to 10 or 20 m.p.h. Thus any creatures living on this cold planet would remain more or less rooted to one spot, instead of flying through the atmosphere at our constant and comfortable speed of 800 m.p.h.

"A spectroscope aboard Earth Explorer II tells us that Earth's atmosphere is composed of a deadly compound made up of oxygen and carbon dioxide. In addition, the majority of the surface of Earth bears a peculiar liquid, chemically H_2O, which is a deadly poison.

"Another startling fact revealed to us by close-up radio telescope pictures is that the light rays from the sun actually penetrate to the surface of Earth, bathing it in sunlight. I don't have to tell you how dangerous this is to life.

"Now we come to the most difficult hurdle to life of all —the rotation of the planet. Any creatures living on Earth must be in a constant state of dizziness. The planet whirls around at a rate 265 times faster than our own planet!

"One final point before we lay to rest forever the myth of life on Earth. Our telemetry equipment noted a very faint residue of radiation in the upper atmosphere, which might point to a series of explosions, thought to be thermonuclear in origin. These explosions were of the type that we developed about 200,000 years ago and abandoned as being too dangerous to our continued existence. The explosions noted were, however, far punier and feebler than our own.

"Some of the younger men of the JPL staff wondered whether this didn't evidence a kind of intelligent life on Earth. But JPL's considered judgment is that any creatures intelligent enough to have developed even so feeble an explosive force would be intelligent enough to see its potential dangers."

If such is the way it may look in the mirror, we ought to take warning. If advanced, intelligent life, or any life at all, is impossible on Venus, *why* is it impossible? Hasty conclusions are notoriously misleading, and perhaps we should look again. Not so long ago pilots of high-flying aircraft were reporting the existence of flying saucers. Does the fact that Americans and Russians have now put their own queer-looking satellites into orbit make flying saucers more or less likely to have been optical illusions? Maybe it's like speech. Man talks so much he hears only the sound of his own voice, never the pregnant silence of a living world. We see now what we are looking for and know to be there: only our own tin cans which steadily accumulate as garbage in our extraterrestrial backyard. Will-o'-the-wisp strangers would hardly be noticed.

In the days when we knew less than we now think we know, when our own flying saucers were still in the comic book stage and it was easier to think of Venus having intelligent inhabitants, the thought that what we could do, some superior Venusians could do better, was more or less plausible. And why shouldn't Venusians have been made in the human image, on land, breathing air, walking on two legs, with a pair of hands, eyes and ears, and generally in unmistakable human shape? Even our gods have been no less. If we had only remained in ignorance of the apparently hostile and barren nature of Venus, and less bound by the rules of biological speculation, we could still use such stuff to make our dreams on.

In all seriousness, what *can* we make of Venus? It is unwise to conclude that no life of any sort exists or has ever existed there, even though this may well be the case. If life of a marginal kind does exist, what may we expect? Once more we are handicapped by the limitations of human imagination which can play only with what it knows, although by scrambling and recombining pieces of the picture we can get the illusion of novelty. Here is what Arthur Clarke, a noted science fiction writer with an enthusiastic interest in interplanetary ventures and a controlled scientific imagination, has suggested in a tale called "Before Eden," which supposes a landing made by two plastic-enclosed men near the south pole of Venus where the temperature is supposed to have dropped below the boiling point of water. A few extracts will do:

" 'This is even better,' said Hutchins, and now there was real excitement in his voice. 'The oxygen concentration's way up—fifteen parts in a million. It was only five back at the car, and down in the lowlands you can scarcely detect it.' 'But fifteen in a *million!*' protested Jerry. 'Nothing could breathe that!' 'You've got hold of the wrong end of the stick,' Hutchins explained. 'Nothing does breathe it. Something *makes* it. Where do you think Earth's oxygen comes from? It's all produced by life—by growing plants. Before there were plants on Earth, our atmosphere was just like this one—a mess of carbon dioxide and ammonia and methane. Then vegetation evolved, and slowly converted the atmosphere into something that animals could breathe.' 'I see,' said Jerry, 'and you think that some process has just started here?' 'It looks like it. *Something* not far from here is producing oxygen—and plant life is the simplest explanation.' [Then they see it] What they were watching was a dark tide, a crawling carpet, sweeping slowly but inexorably toward them over the top of the ridge. . . . So far, the thing had shown no signs that it was aware of their presence. It had merely flowed forward like the mindless tide that it almost certainly was. Apart from the fact that it climbed over small obstacles, it might have been an advancing flood of water. . . . It was sweeping over the ground, as the shadow moves before the wind—and where it had rested, the rocks were pitted with innumerable tiny holes that might have been etched by acid, 'Yes,' said Hutchins, when Jerry remarked about this. 'That's how some lichens feed; they secrete acids that dissolve rock.'

". . . This world around them was no longer the same; Venus was no longer dead—it had joined Earth and Mars. For life called to life, across the gulfs of space. Everything that grew or moved upon the face of any planet was a portent, a promise that Man was not alone in the universe of blazing suns and swirling nebulae. If as yet he had found no companions with whom he could speak, that was only to be expected, for the light-years and the ages still stretched before him, waiting to be explored. Meanwhile, he must guard and cherish the life he found, whether it be upon Earth or Mars or Venus. . . .

"For a while nothing moved in the greenly glimmering, fogbound landscape; it was deserted by man and crimson carpet alike. Then, flowing over the wind-carved hills, the creature reappeared. Or perhaps it was another of the same species; no one would ever know. . . . And then it stopped.

"It was not puzzled, for it had no mind. But the chemical urges that drove it relentlessly over the polar plateau were crying: Here, here! Somewhere close at hand was the most precious of all foods it needed—phosphorus, the element without which the spark of life could never ignite. It began to nuzzle rocks, to ooze into the cracks and crannies, to scratch and scrabble with probing tendrils. Nothing that it did was beyond the capacity of any plant or tree on Earth—but it moved a

thousand times more quickly, requiring only minutes
to reach its goal and pierce through the plastic film.

"And then it feasted, on food more concentrated than
any it had ever known. It absorbed the carbohydrates
and the proteins and the phosphates, the nicotine from
the cigarette ends, the cellulose from the paper cups and
spoons. All these it broke down and assimilated into its
strange body, without difficulty and without harm.

"Likewise it absorbed a whole microscosmos of living
creatures—the bacteria and viruses which, upon an older
planet, had evolved a thousand deadly strains. Though
only a very few could survive in this heat and this atmosphere, they were sufficient. As the carpet crawled back to
the lake, it carried contagion to all its world. . . . Beneath
the clouds of Venus, the Story of Creation was ended."

What can we make of this? Certainly the life described
is little more than minimal. The questions are whether
life of this sort could exist on Venus, and what earthly
forms of life are the inspiration for an imagined form of
this kind. What, in other words, is implied in the appearance and activities of the crawling carpet or, as the author
called it, botany on the run? The sensitivity and rapid
movement of the mobile carpet in such arid circumstances
virtually rules out growth based upon fluidity, whether or
not the result of cell division as in most terrestrial organisms, even such growth as is seen in the overnight upshoot-
ing of mushrooms and toadstools. The nearest thing to
this sort of movement we know here on Earth is that of
Amoeba, which is a one-celled aquatic animal that literally
flows in one direction or another in search for food, which
it engulfs in an enveloping movement. But Amoeba is
microscopic, rarely visible to the naked eye. A larger organism which moves in much the same way and is some-

what more plant-like is the slime mold that lives among decaying leaves and wood, feeding on bacteria and particles of decay. Sheets and strands of slime mold may be inches long, with no cell boundaries to impede internal flowing movements. Flow they do, but so imperceptibly that you might watch for hours to see one advance a fraction of its own length. Could such a small, filmy sheet of living substance grow as large as an acre and still function in a flowing way? It does not seem possible, for the same sort of reasons that you cannot make an elephant as small as a flea, or a flea as large as an elephant. Changing the size of an organism to such an extent creates all sorts of biological engineering problems which generally cannot be solved.

The Venus carpet is described as a multicolored, photosynthetic, oxygen-producing organism. On Earth, the photosynthetic parts of plants are green, which means that they reflect green light and absorb the spectral light on either side of the green. However, no good reason appears to exist why the green component of sunlight is not used—in fact some photosynthetic bacteria are purple and do employ the green—and therefore vegetative life on another planet could well be all the colors of the rainbow, or any one of them. Earth's atmospheric oxygen is generally believed to be almost entirely a byproduct of plant photosynthesis. It should also be present in the Venusian atmosphere if water is split up by the photosynthetic process.

Again, the carpet is described as emerging from a lake on a foray primarily for minerals, especially phosphorus. Rockbound lichens here do obtain essential minerals by dissolving underlying rock with acids, and phosphorus is truly the spark of life, the most vital of all the essential elements that make up the protoplasm of all the life of Earth. But etching rocks is about as slow a process as absorbing water from soil by roots. Neither activity is conducive to flowing happily across a landscape.

Then there is the matter of water. If we assume that a lake with life in it is necessarily water, a further incompatibility arises. A truly aquatic organism, whether plant or animal or something which may be both or neither, if it is primarily and primitively aquatic and not an invader from the land, is typically naked-skinned and in chemical balance with the watery solution in which it lives. To be out of water usually means sudden death. A protective outer layer, sufficient to prevent loss of water when exposed to the atmosphere, generally confers an external stiffness incompatible with fluid motion. Slime molds survive in their active state only when humidity is maximal, so that water loss is minimal. Where little or no water vapor exists, dessication would be immediate unless the living material was encapsulated in some way. The lichens, which are the only terrestrial vegetation found from pole to pole, in the deserts, and high up the mountains, are notoriously immobile and slow of growth, and well encased within a tough, dry outer layer which completely conserves the internal moisture.

As for water itself, the only life of which we know anything at all is the life of Earth, and even the driest forms of life, in active state, consist mostly of water. Of the wetter forms, a jellyfish may consist of 98 per cent water, with only 2 per cent minerals and organic substance to transform the water into organized jellyfish. It is difficult even to think of living things which do not contain water as a principal ingredient, which have not originally evolved in water, and do not depend on the availability of at least some water from some source. Even if we could theoretically dispense with water and substitute some other medium for life to be based on and exist in, at least to begin with, we should have to postulate that it be fluid. The internal activity and mobility of protoplasm, which is what we recognize as being living or vital, demands liquidity of a sort. Hydrocarbons might serve. But on Venus even the heaviest hydrocarbon would probably be vaporized at temperatures above the boiling point of water and we are left with much the same problem. Whether life of any kind can exist on Venus therefore appears to hang on whether water can exist there in liquid form. If the surface of Venus, even on the dark side, is as hot as the Mariner reported, the possibility of surface water anywhere, including the poles, seems remote indeed. And so with life.

If Venus is barren or dead, we are still interested in why this should be, for we are deeply concerned with the nature of the solar system as a whole. Both Venus and Earth are highly significant parts. We ourselves, as a particular kind of life, are a product. And we are already dreaming about ways of making inhospitable Venus habitable by introducing certain Earthly organisms that may transform its atmosphere and thereby lower the surface temperature. The dream exists and seems fantastic, but it is no less remarkable than the dreamer.

The discovery of the high surface temperature of Venus came as a surprise. The outer surface of Venus' cloud layer, the albedo, which reflects most of the sunrays reaching the planet and is responsible for its brilliance in the sky at dawn and dusk, thirteen thousand times as bright as the full Moon, is about −30° F. on both the light and dark side. Beneath the cloud layer, which is about fifteen miles thick and apparently forty-five miles above the planet's surface, the temperature is about 200° F., just short of the boiling point of water. At the surface the temperature is reported to be about 800° F. Microwave data indicate that the surface itself is relatively smooth and hard, and resembles terrestrial desert waste land. The high temperature and the surface hardness rule out the previously suggested and more interesting possibilities that Venus is covered by Coal Age-type swamps, a planetary oil field, or a global ocean of carbonated water. All that we now know of Venus makes it seem impossible that life of any kind exists there or has ever existed. Venus in fact appears to be dead in more ways than one.

Evidence from radio telescopes seems to show that Venus, as with Mercury, either keeps one face to the Sun during the course of its 225 Earth-day year, as the Moon does to Earth, or even fails to turn to this extent. Why, then, does the dark side stay so hot? The proposed explanation is that winds in the dense atmosphere circulate the heat, and the thick hydrocarbon clouds provide effective insulation.

The proposal to transform the veil of Venus into one capable of supporting life may remain forever the dream it is now. If it is sheer fantasy, so until recently was the project to direct a complex instrument to fly past Venus and have it send back detailed scientific information, although one such miracle does not prove the possibility of another. Hope is further encouraged by the discovery, from photographs taken through balloon-telescopes 87,500 feet above the Earth's surface, a year or so later than the Mariner made its report, that considerable water vapor does exist above the cloud deck of Venus, nearly as much as occurs in the Earth's atmosphere at a comparable level.

We begin with the facts that the thick cloud layer of Venus has a greenhouse effect. The clouds may be hydrocarbon droplets similar to water droplets in Earthly clouds, which condense in the cool top of the atmosphere but stay in vapor form in the lower parts. In this case the dark Venusian surface has clear, compressed, oily air. Or the clouds may yet turn out to be water clouds like our own.

In either case the Sun's shorter infra-red waves penetrate all the way, just as they do into a greenhouse. Once inside the cover they are modified by carbon dioxide so that they cannot escape, and the heat builds up. The energy is trapped. If then the carbon dioxide, which is known to be more than 1,000 times greater than water vapor in the Venusian atmosphere, could be broken down, a very different situation might prevail. Certainly the experiment would be worth trying, once we have discovered all that is possible concerning Venus as she is.

Such a transformation might be accomplished by a terrestrial organism that could carry on photosynthesis in some part of the outer atmosphere of Venus where the heat is not excessive. Only microörganisms could remain aloft to become a fairly permanent aerial population, as a certain kind of red bacterium does here on Earth in the thin atmosphere eighty miles above the surface.

Since there is no liquid water on Venus, the organism must be able to utilize water vapor from the atmosphere or ice crystals from the cloud layer. The only known organisms which photosynthesize and liberate molecular oxygen are the algae. The organism would also have to be resistant to extremes of temperature. The blue-green algae, which may well be survivors from Earth's own beginnings, are the most suitable prospects, for some are known to survive immersion in liquid nitrogen and some ordinarily live in hot springs at 175° F., which would parboil almost all other forms of life. Unless there is ammonia in the atmosphere of Venus, the organisms would also have to fix free atmospheric nitrogen in order to survive. The only photosynthetic, nitrogen-fixing, oxygen-evolving, temperature-resistant aerial microörganisms are the blue-green algae of the Nostoc kind, small enough to remain suspended in the dense Venusian clouds. If the upper atmosphere of Venus were successfully seeded by organisms of this sort, the outcome could be a fall in the carbon dioxide content, a lessening of the greenhouse effect, and a lowering of the surface temperature. Eventually the surface temperature might fall to below the boiling point of water, soon to be followed by rain and the accumulation of a few inches of surface water. This could well lead to surface temperatures not far from what we are accustomed to, together with a breatheable atmosphere and the beginnings of a terrestrial vegetation. At least it is something to think about.

Moonstruck

THOUGH THE SUN sustain us with heat and light and is our
Star of Destiny, the Moon, the Silver Goddess, Diana of
the Heavens, is she who makes us giddy. Sun worshipers
we may have been but moon gazers we certainly are, and
but for this no one would have thought of calling human
beings the only funny things in the universe. Undoubtedly
our lunar rhythms add spice to the daily round of our
existence.

To the extent that the Moon governs our lives we are
lunatics, literally moonstruck. Bewitching or baleful, without her we would have slept more soundly at nights and
human history might have taken a different turn. Even
now, perhaps especially now, in this age of supposed ration-
ality and sophistication, we look up to the Moon completely hypnotized and yearn to possess her. The mountains of the Moon have called to man's imagination
throughout the ages, ever since the Greeks recognized them
twenty-five hundred years ago, though the superstitious
Middle Ages saw things differently.

Speculation concerning trips to the Moon and elsewhere

became a serious subject following the significant year 1609. The reign of Elizabeth I, with its voyages and trans-oceanic discoveries, had already come to its end. And so had the old Ptolemaic view of the universe, sacred to the heart of Christendom, which held the Earth to be the stationary center of all things, with the Sun, planets, and stars circling around her in orderly precession.

The Danish astronomer, Tycho Brahe, during the last decades of the sixteenth century, had already recorded the successive positions of Mars with marvelous accuracy. Now came John Kepler who, believing that Earth actually traveled around the Sun, plotted the paths of both Earth and Mars and found them to be ellipses rather than the expected circles. He also discovered that the speed with which a planet traverses its ellipse varies in a regular way, accelerating when approaching closer to the Sun and decelerating when moving farther away, just as our own man-made satellites do as they swing high and low during their rounds of the Earth. He saw the mountains of the Moon for what they were, and he thought he saw seas comparable to the oceans of Earth, as many observers have done since.

Kepler was the first to determine where any planet would be in relation to other planets at any time, and so laid the navigational groundwork for the age of interplanetary probes and travel now beginning. Even so, he was surrounded by medieval irrationality.

During the summer of 1609 he made out a plan for actually landing on the Moon, concerning which he wrote to Galileo the following year but could not talk about openly because the Lutheran Church was as hot after celestial-minded heretics as was the Catholic Church in Italy. Nevertheless word got out, and his mother was tried, though not executed, as a witch responsible for Kepler's devil-inspired ideas.

To start with, he decided that neither frail nor fat persons would be eligible for the ride but only lean hard bodies well used to a Spartan diet, the same requirements imposed on our contemporary astronauts. The technique of space travel he left well enough alone, being aware that in this respect he was long before his time, but he was prophetic with regard to navigational questions and the hazard to life. As a student of light, heat, and optics Kepler realized that, although outer space was an unheated vacuum, the unfiltered rays of the Sun would soon disintegrate an unshielded man. Therefore the voyage to the Moon should be made within the shadow cast by the Earth. The Earth throws a cone-shaped shadow away from the Sun that cuts off more than ninety-nine per cent of the Sun's radiation. Kepler himself had previously concluded that the gravity pull of the Moon is responsible for the Earth's oceanic tides and he now went further to say that if the Moon so affects the Earth's oceans, a similar pull would operate on bodies suspended between Earth and Moon, and a space vessel would be drawn toward the Moon once escape from Earth had been effected. And nearly two centuries before Joseph Priestley identified oxygen, Kepler declared that man would have to take with him a means of breathing the vital element of animate life. None of this was wild imagination, but the clear, controlled imagination of a disciplined thinker and scientist foreshadowing by more than three centuries what is now engrossing much of mankind.

Kepler was less interested in the Moon as a celestial object of curiosity, let alone a place to be colonized, than as a vantage-place from which to observe the Earth. This may eventually be our own major interest, inasmuch as the Moon as a satellite planet offers limited scope for inquiry but unlimited opportunity for astronomical examination of the universe unimpeded by terrestrial atmospheric disturbance, a far better base for instruments than any man-made orbiting satellites are ever likely to be. Kepler, however, merely wanted to get far enough away from the Earth, in imagination at least, to see it in perspective as a planet revolving around its own axis, four times the breadth of the Moon and fifteen times its brilliance, and waxing and waning as the Moon does from here. This is a perspective we would all be the better to have, for a view of the lonely Earth from outer space would make us cuddle closer and cherish it better.

The Moon itself, of course, had to be habitable if human beings were to stand there to watch the revolving Earth, and so Kepler assumed it would have its own inhabitants. He imagined the lunar inhabitants to have thick, porous, husk-like skins, necessary to prevent fatal evaporation on a planet devoid of atmosphere, and to be aquatic, sinuous creatures suited to life in a watery world of submerged caverns, a concept of fitness to the environment that became familiar thinking only after Darwin developed the idea at a later time. The later speculators on the nature of possible Moon inhabitants have in fact done no better.

Jules Verne, writing in 1865, just a few years after the publication of Darwin's *Origin of Species,* when evolutionary thinking was catching fire, was generally more sensible than his successors in science fiction who have peopled the Moon without real regard for its limitations. His description of light and shade on the Moon need little revision. In his own words:

> "no twilight on her surface; night following day and day following night with the suddenness of a lamp which is extinguished or lighted amidst profound darkness— no transition from cold to heat, the temperature falling

in an instant from boiling point to the cold of space. Another consequence of the want of air is that absolute darkness reigns where the sun's rays do not penetrate. That which on earth is called diffusion of light—that luminous matter which the air holds in suspension, which creates the twilight and the daybreak, which produces the umbrae and penumbrae and all the magic of chiaroscuro—does not exist on the moon. Hence the harshness of contrasts, which only admit of two colors, black and white."

Then the landscape itself:

"Circles, craters, and uprooted mountains succeeded each other incessantly. No more plains; no more seas. . . . And lastly, in the center of this region of crevasses, the most splendid mountain on the lunar disc, the dazzling Tycho, in which posterity will ever preserve the name of the illustrious Danish astronomer. . . . Tycho forms such a concentration of light that the inhabitants of the earth can see it without glasses, though at a distance of 240,000 miles! . . . Tycho belongs to the system of radiating mountains, like Aristarchus and Copernicus; but it is the most complete and decided of all, showing unquestionably the frightful volcanic action to which the formation of the moon is due. . . . Nature had not left the bottom of this crater flat and empty. It possessed its own peculiar orography—a mountainous system, making it a world in itself. . . . In all directions ran luminous furrows, raised at the edges and concave at the center, some twelve others thirty miles across. These brilliant trains extended in some places to within six hundred miles of Tycho, and seemed to cover, particularly toward the east, the northeast and the north, half of the Southern Hemisphere. One of these jets extended as far as the circle of Neander, situated on the fortieth meridian. Another by a slight curve furrowed the Sea of Nectar, breaking against the chain of Pyrenees, after a circuit of eight hundred miles. Others, toward the west, covered the Sea of Clouds and the Sea of Humors with a luminous network. What was the origin of these sparkling rays which shone on the plains as well as on the reliefs, at whatever height they may be? All started from a common center, the crater of Tycho. They sprang from him."

The smallest telescope or binoculars will show the accuracy of this vivid account. And the question stands, for the secret of Tycho, whether its origin is volcanic or meteoritic, is the secret of the moon itself. Jules Verne went on to speculate about the moon as a habitat for life, in the form of a discussion among members of his expedition to the moon:

" 'I believe, indeed I affirm, that the moon has been inhabited by a human race organized like our own, that she has produced animals anatomically formed like the terrestrial animals; but I add that these races, human or animal, have had their day, are now forever extinct!'

" 'Then,' asked Michel, 'the moon must be older than the earth?'

" 'No!' said Barbicane decidedly. 'But it is a world which has grown older quicker and whose formation and deformation have been more rapid. Relatively, the organizing force of matter has been much more violent in the interior of the moon than in the interior of the terrestrial globe. The actual state of this cracked, twisted, and burst disc abundantly proves this. The moon and the earth were nothing but gaseous masses originally. These gases have passed into a liquid state under differ-

ent influences, and the solid masses have been formed
later. But most certainly our sphere was still gaseous or
liquid when the moon, solidified by cooling, had become habitable.'

" 'I believe it,' said Nicholl.

" 'Then,' continued Barbicane, 'an atmosphere surrounded it, the waters contained within this gaseous
envelope could not evaporate. Under the influence of
air, water, light, solar heat, and central heat, vegetation
took possession of the continents prepared to receive it;
and certainly life showed itself at about this period, for
nature does not expend herself in vain; and a world so
wonderfully formed for habitation must necessarily be
inhabited.'

" 'But,' said Nicholl, 'many phenomena inherent in
our satellite might cramp the expansion of the animal
and vegetable kingdoms. For example, its days and
nights of 354 hours?'

" 'At the terrestrial poles they last six months,' said
Michel.

" 'An argument of little value, since the poles are not
inhabited.'

" 'Let us observe, my friends,' said Barbicane, 'that if
in the actual state of the moon its long nights and long
days created differences of temperature insupportable to
organization, it was not so at the historical period of
time. The atmosphere enveloped the disc with a fluid
mantle; vapor deposited itself in the shape of clouds;
this natural screen tempered the ardor of the solar rays
and retained the nocturnal radiation. Light, like heat,
can diffuse itself in the air; hence an equality between
the influences which no longer exists now that atmosphere has almost entirely disappeared. And now I am
going to astonish you.'

" 'Astonish us?' said Michel Arden.

" 'I firmly believe that at the period when the moon was inhabited, the nights and days did not last 354 hours!'

" 'And why?' asked Nicholl quickly.

" 'Because then most probably the rotary motion of the moon upon her axis was not equal to her revolution, an equality which presents each part of her disc during fifteen days to the action of the solar rays.'

" 'Granted,' replied Nicholl, 'but why should not these two motions have been equal, as they are really so?'

" 'Because that equality has only been determined by terrestrial attraction. And who can say that this attraction was powerful enough to alter the motion of the moon at that period when the earth was still fluid?'

" 'Just so,' said Nicholl, 'and who can say that the moon has always been a satellite of the earth?'

" 'And who can say,' exclaimed Michel Arden, 'that the moon did not exist before the earth?'

"Their imaginations carried them away into an indefinite field of hypothesis. Barbicane sought to restrain them.

" 'Those speculations are too high,' said he, 'problems utterly insoluble. Do not let us enter upon them. Let us only admit the insufficiency of the primordial attraction; and then by the inequality of the two motions of rotation and revolution, the days and nights could have succeeded each other on the moon as they succeed each other on the earth. Besides, even without these conditions, life was possible.'

" 'And so,' asked Michel Arden, 'humanity has disappeared from the moon?'

" 'Yes,' replied Barbicane, 'after having doubtless remained persistently for millions of centuries; by degrees

the atmosphere becoming rarefied, the disc became uninhabitable, as the terrestrial globe will one day by
cooling.'

" 'By cooling?'

" 'Certainly,' replied Barbicane, 'as the internal fires
became extinguished, and the incandescent matter concentrated itself, the lunar crust cooled. By degrees the
consequences of these phenomena showed themselves in
the disappearance of organized beings, and by the disappearance of vegetation. Soon the atmosphere was rarefied, probably withdrawn by terrestrial attraction; then
aerial departure of respirable air, and disappearance of
water by means of evaporation. At this period the moon
becoming uninhabitable, was no longer inhabited. It
was a dead world, as we see it to-day.' "

Leaving the question of life aside, this account of Verne's
is revealing. There is little or no doubt that the Moon at
one time did rotate about its own axis at a rate probably
comparable to the rate of the spin of the Earth. And that
this spin became progressively slowed down by the gravitational pull of the Earth acting on the body of the Moon in
the same way as the Moon even now exerts its tidal effects
on the Earth. This would be so whether or not Earth and
the Moon had ever been in a liquid state, for the Moon
produces a tidal wave not only in the terrestrial oceans but
in the atmosphere and in the crust itself. Likewise the
Earth has produced tidal friction on the Moon under all
circumstances and, being much the larger body, has had
by far the greater braking action of the two, and the Moon
being much the smaller has been by far the more suscepti-
ble. Even so, the braking action of the Moon on the Earth
is far from negligible, has already retarded the Earthly spin
to some extent, and may at long last seal the fate of the

Earth. The Sun also exerts a tidal effect on the Earth, of comparable magnitude to that of the Moon, and were it not for the relatively long distance of the Earth from the Sun the solar tides and braking action would be much greater. Venus and Mercury, so much closer to the Sun, have been subject to solar tides to a far greater degree, and apparently at some time already long past have lost their spin in the same way as the Moon. And Venus and the Moon, at least, are without a magnetic field, whatever that may signify.

When Moon and Earth were very young, both were spinning on their axis at a more exuberant rate and would have been considerably closer together. George Darwin, grandson of Charles, suggested that the Moon was flung off from the outer parts of the Earth, specifically from that part which is now the basin of the Pacific Ocean, as a result of excessive spin by a somewhat fluid Earth. In spite of the persisting popularity of this mother-daughter relationship, too much is now known about the ocean floor for the proposal to be seriously considered. Nor is the picture presented by Jules Verne, of Earth and Moon condensing from a gaseous state through liquid to a solid condition, now generally accepted. Most astronomers now believe that Earth and Moon were formed separately, like other planets, and that each accumulated from debris that once formed a vast, turbulent cloud, the central regions of which collected to form the Sun. They were formed cold. Heat came later.

Earth, like Venus, is massive enough to hold on to a relatively dense atmosphere. The Moon, only one eightieth as massive, cannot hold any but the heaviest gases and no atmosphere has ever been detected, except for a brief, localized emission of gas from the center of the crater Alphonsus and elsewhere. Erosion of surface features caused

by water and wind is absent on the Moon, but small meteorites, which disintegrate in Earth's atmosphere, erode the
surface.

The main features of the Moon—the giant craters, the
mountainous ridges radiating across the planet, and the
flat areas, miscalled seas—have been the subject of a running debate for many years. Jules Verne poses the question: are the craters of volcanic or meteoritic origin?
Elsewhere in his book he describes the arrival and impact
of a large meteor, which explodes with the intensity of an
atomic bomb. This seems to be the explanation of many
of the lunar craters, which are clearly of impact origin, for
the Moon encounters meteorites at velocities often as high
as fifty miles per second and, in such collisions, the meteorites would not penetrate far before the compressed rocks
would vaporize and explode, throwing aside masses of
rock debris much larger than the original meteorites. The
chains of craters which are seen on the Moon may well
have been caused by similar explosions, though of lunar
origin. Whatever their source, meteoritic or internally produced, their explosive origin seems certain, as though they
were giant lunar bubbles exploding into the vacuum of
outer space.

How the Moon has come to be what it is, is a crucial
question. The history of any planet would throw light on
planets in general, and even though the Moon may be
among the least of them, it is closest to home and is in
certain ways more open to examination than Earth herself.
Our concern is not just with this planet or that, but with
the nature of the solar system as a whole, and so of the
possibility of solar systems throughout the universe. As an
abode of life the Moon, without air or water, seems as un-
promising as it could be. Yet this very fact is our opportunity, for why should two planets so close together as

Moon and Earth be so different? Analysis of meteorites arriving on Earth indicates that materially the solar system is all of one piece and one age, that the whole system formed some 4,600 million years ago, and that the planets and other solid bodies of the solar system have grown by an accumulation of smaller pre-existent particles and dust in a solid state and at moderate temperatures not very different from what we now experience. When so much alike in origin and age, why are they so different with regard to atmosphere and water? The relatively small size of the Moon seems to account for the loss of gaseous atmosphere into space in the course of time, since the Moon's force of gravity appears to be too weak to hold one within bounds. Water is another matter.

Galileo and the other early telescopic observers have been taken to task by later observers for misnaming the lunar flatlands as seas. Certainly these areas are not open oceans, but what they are remains a question. One theory is that they are extensive lava flows that have welled up through the Moon's crust, often to cover enormous areas. This may be so, but the possibility of water cannot be dismissed so lightly, for water may be present in other than liquid form. In fact, our ideas concerning the source of the water forming the seas of the Earth have changed during recent times. Instead of regarding terrestrial water as having originally precipitated from the atmosphere during an early cooling of a hot Earth, it is now believed to be entirely a product from the Earth's interior, squeezed from the rocky material of the deep crust through volcanic cracks and progressively accumulating at the surface.

Water has been present in the solar system dust apparently from the beginning, for the solid meteoritic debris still drifting in space around us retains a significant amount of water in its substance. There is little doubt that the

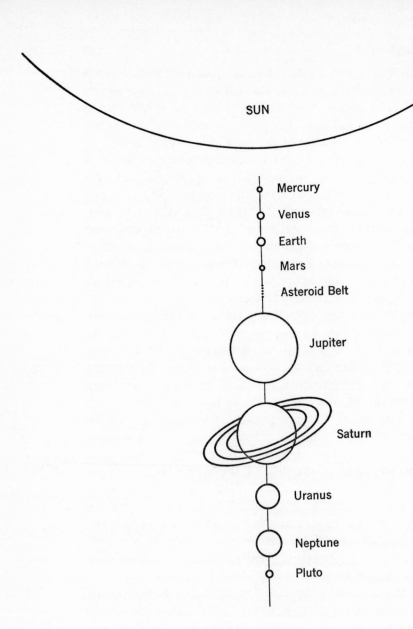

SUN

Mercury

Venus

Earth

Mars

Asteroid Belt

Jupiter

Saturn

Uranus

Neptune

Pluto

Planet Sizes

Moon originally possessed as much water, proportionately, as the Earth. Has she lost it, or hoarded it? The answer depends on what has happened and may still be happening inside the Moon, just as much of what so vitally concerns us at the surface of the Earth depends on the workings of the Earth's interior.

The surface of the Earth is warm where the Sun's rays strike it, but the Earth's crust is also warm far below the depth to which the solar warmth can reach. The heat in fact increases with the depth so that in the deepest mines, which are relatively little more than a shallow scratching of the crust, the temperature is much too high for comfort. This heat does not come from the Sun, nor is it a leftover from a hot Earthly infancy. It is produced by radioactive decay of the uranium, thorium, and some potassium present in the crust. These same elements are almost certainly present in the matter of the Moon, and inevitably produce heat as they spontaneously decay. Yet the outer crust of the Moon, like that of the Earth, is a poor conductor of heat, so that the interior of both planets must be slowly warming up. This heat is more than sufficient to expel the water molecules bound in the substance of crystalline rocks and drive them under their own pressure, as superheated steam, along any crack or fissure opening outward. There is little doubt that the deep interior of the Moon must by now be almost completely dessicated, and its outer crust correspondingly enriched with water. How close to the surface can this water be?

Radiowave analysis of the Moon's surface shows that two to three feet below the surface, where the heat waves of the long lunar-day Sun cannot penetrate, the temperature is almost constant and is about as cold as the Earth's North Pole in winter. Even hot steam slowly seeping outward through the lunar crust would condense into a liquid and freeze into ice before it reached the surface. All this leaves the Moon's surface as dry as we have thought it to be, but the low bulges found in clusters in great numbers on the visible surface may be subsurface glaciers covered with dust and other debris. Calculations allowing for evaporation of surface ice into outer space during the entire lifetime of the Moon show that probably no more than one tenth of the squeezed out and frozen water would have been lost by this means. Accordingly, liquid water itself must be present at some depth beneath the surface. Subterranean—or sublunar—water, whether glacial or hot or in between, completely cut off from solar radiation, is not likely to have evolved any form of life. All the same, Kepler's and Jules Verne's concepts of aquatic forms of life adapted to living in submerged caverns now appear to be more inspired than ludicrous. In any case, the possibility of finding frozen water at or close to the surface of the Moon is of the utmost importance in connection with establishing manned astronomical outposts of the Earth.

Apart from the possible accessibility of water in some form, landings on the Moon may be surprisingly soft. Radiowave studies by both Americans and Russians show that the lunar surface is transparent to such waves to a depth of several yards. The suggestion is made that the Moon may be covered with a filmy layer, like cotton candy, of a sort formed by foam cells that have burst and released their gas, or a honeycomb with walls intact and the gas inside. A highly porous surface could have been produced by the melting of crustal surface matter from meteor impacts, not unlike the exploded craters resulting from giant meteors, but on a miniature scale and infinitely more numerous. The Moon after all has no atmosphere to cushion meteors of any size, and even the smallest must impinge like bul-

lets, except for meteoritic dust that has no weight to speak
of.

The finest dust travels through space, not merely with
such initial momentum as it may have had, nor only by being drawn by gravitational force to larger bodies of matter
such as planets or stars or dusty condensations, but driven
by the pressure of light itself. This is also true of the spores
of living organisms that may escape beyond the Earth's atmosphere, for they are of an order of size small enough to
be subject to the pressure of this radiation. These two facts
have been known for a long time, and several decades ago
served as the basis for a theory concerning the origin of life
on Earth. Such spores, which are known to be incessantly
drifting in inconceivable numbers in the atmosphere, forever settling and coming alive in the damper places of the
Earth, including the nasal passages of human beings, drift
to high levels in the atmosphere and probably escape, to be
driven outward into space by the light of the Sun. If this is
the rule, then space must have been contaminated with the
drifting spores of life ever since the first planet in the universe produced them. Life on Earth, in its primary form,
was supposed to come from such a source, and the actual
origin of life was therefore pushed far back into space and
time, out of reach. As a theory, this was intellectually un-
satisfying, because it shelved the question without answer-
ing it. Other hypotheses have since taken its place, with the
basic assumption that the life of the Earth originated and
evolved as the direct outcome of the Earth's matter under
the Earth's circumstances at the time. In any case, most of
the spores of microscopic organisms that normally live at
the surface of the Earth are killed by high-level solar or
cosmic radiation and are unlikely to survive passage in
space. Nevertheless, the discovery of bacteria actually living
in the outer atmosphere not far from the level of the orbit-

ing astronauts must be taken seriously, for some spores of microörganisms may accordingly survive a transit. Spores and most other kinds of cells can readily survive the extreme cold of such a trip.

Always, however, the drift would be from the Sun, or any sun, toward the outer parts of a solar system. By this token the Moon may have been collecting living spore dust as well as other dust during its own passage through space, and this dust may just possibly survive in still viable form in the porous lunar crust. Because of this and other possibilities, the Moon itself must on no account be contaminated by any instruments we may send there, or confusion will reign. All must be sterilized from start to finish.

The pressure of sunlight is by no means to be ignored. It pushed the first Vanguard satellite some miles out of what would otherwise have been its orbit, and in the case of Echo I, which was a sphere 100 feet in diameter, the low point of its orbit was pushed down several hundred miles in a few months. Pressure as effective as this may be put to use. No less a professional than the director of the Office of Space Sciences of the National Aeronautics and Space Administration has predicted that Solar Sailing will become an actuality, for instruments if not for men. Once a satellite has been put into orbit, say 1,000 miles up where it will not be slowed by the drag of the air, instruments could unfold an extensive circular, metal-plated sail with a small compact electronic rudder and other radio equipment suspended to it. Somewhat in the manner of a ship sailing into the wind, the Solar Sail could even make progress toward the Sun, by alternately sailing and coasting away and toward the Sun in an ever-widening spiral from the point of departure. It could be a very effective way of taking scientific measurements throughout a tremendous volume of space surrounding the Earth, say, between the Earth and

Venus, where the Sun's atmosphere extends to the Earth. Or such Solar Sails might monitor the route of the short trip to the Moon, serving as a traffic check in days to come and reporting the fluctuating radiative and meteoritic hazards of the cosmic climate. Curiouser and curiouser, said Alice.

Outward Bound

THE GREATEST SPECTATOR SPORT of all time has already started. Russians and Americans compete to put a man into space, each successively improving on the last performance of the other, with man on the Moon the enchanting prospect. Dr. Wernher von Braun, among the first and foremost in the rocket game in war and peace, foresees the Moon, by the middle of the next century, as a fine place to spend a honeymoon, to gamble, and to go prospecting—not necessarily all at once or in that order. Even if making the Moon into a bigger and better Nevada, a state with a distinctly lunar tinge to its landscape and to the behavior of its more temporary residents, should be a worthy object, Dr. von Braun seems to underestimate the price of a ticket, let alone a few other considerations. Moon tickets will become cheaper, no doubt, but the initial cost is so high that excursion rates are likely to appear exorbitant even to millionaires.

Landing the first man on the Moon, with a valid return ticket in his pocket, will be the most expensive trip of all. Dr. Warren Weaver has pointed out that the sum of

$30 billion, which is merely a provisional underestimate of
the total cost, is a sum so large that the ordinary human being simply cannot grasp its magnitude except by looking at
the alternative things it could purchase: "With that sum
one could give a 10 per cent raise in salary, over a ten-year
period, to every teacher in the U.S. from kindergarten
through universities (about $9.8 billion required); could
give $10 million each to 200 of the better smaller colleges
($2 billion required); could finance seven-year fellowships
(freshman through Ph.D.) at $4,000 per person per year for
50,000 new scientists and engineers ($1.4 billion required);
could contribute $200 million each toward the creation of
ten new medical schools ($2 billion required); could build
and largely endow complete universities with liberal arts,
medical, engineering, and agricultural faculties for all fifty-
three of the nations which have been added to the United
Nations since its original founding ($13.2 billion re-
quired); could create three more permanent Rockefeller
Foundations ($1.5 billion required); and one would still
have left $100 million for a program of informing the pub-
lic about science." As the editor of *Science,* Dr. Philip
Abelson, has said, "Manned exploration of the Moon has
only one justification: to satisfy man's spirit of adventure;
. . . the billions of dollars now being spent on the Moon
race will not advance scientific knowledge as rapidly as
knowledge might be advanced without sending a man to
the Moon. I believe it is realistic to say that the manned
lunar program will be carried to a successful conclusion in
spite of the wasted time and cost; but let's be clear. This
isn't science. It's adventure and propaganda." So, for better or worse, we seem to be on our way, to the Moon and
beyond.

Man-in-Space poses two very different problems. How to
get from here to some place else. And how to survive the

trip and also some sort of visit. Presumably the questions
of navigation and propulsion are no longer serious, at least
within our immediate cosmic neighborhood. If instruments
can be sent and to some degree steered to Venus and to the
back of the Moon, sending a larger package with one or
more men aboard is only a matter of time. Navigation
should become easier, not any more difficult. The survival
and return of a man on such a trip is something else. Monkeys, dogs, and mice will lead the way and the first intima-
tion that a man could stand the trip to the Moon or Mars
may be an electrocardiogram radioed back from a hapless
chimpanzee on an expendable one-way journey. Before we
venture our own precious bodies that far, not yours or
mine of course but that of some heroic, superstable, well
trained, optimistic guy who has either been brainwashed or
has nothing to lose, the short trips to the Moon may have
become commonplace and we will know much more about
the prospects of survival.

With so much money and effort involved, it is clearly
vital to the whole business, as well as reasonably humane,
to bring the bodies back alive, even though a call for sui-
cide volunteers would undoubtedly be answered. Consequently the human body in health is now undergoing its
most intensive investigation in the history of physiological
science. With so exciting a vision ahead—the conquest of
space—innumerable young men are apparently willing to
serve as human guinea pigs in this connection and put up
with somewhat humiliating physiological treatment, as the
first step toward hitching the wagon to a star. Human
guinea pigs are of course not alone. The whole living
kingdom is under compulsion to supply candidates for in-
vestigations into space biology. In fact there are no holds
barred, for Man-in-Space in the long run means man on
another planet. Getting away from the Earth is not enough

by itself, except to get a better view of the ancestral home, and the expense would hardly justify that as the only objective, at least in the eyes of those who pay for it. Keeping man alive where he has no business to be and trying to anticipate what he may encounter in the strange environments of other planets is the modest program of those in charge of that branch of science already known as exobiology.

An advertisement which appeared in the *Bulletin of the American Institute of Biological Sciences,* placed there by the National Aeronautics and Space Administration, presents as good a synopsis as any of the somewhat overwhelming scope of the subject:

"For the guidance of biologists, the Biosciences Program, Office of Space Sciences, NASA, has issued this list of its interests:

"*Exobiology Program.* Ground-based and in-flight experiments to identify and study extraterrestrial life and to determine the type of analysis necessary for such identification. Analysis and development of space probe decontamination methods, ground-based research on the origin of organic compounds (protobiochemistry), analysis of meteorites for organic constituents, distribution and characterization of microbes in the upper terrestrial atmosphere, infra-red spectroscopic analysis of the planets, and the design and flight of experiments for the detection and study of life on other planets."

There it is in a nutshell. We have come a long way since Darwin opened the door to the evolutionary way of thought. Yet there is more to it, particularly with regard to studies of man and other terrestrial organisms in relation to their survival in space. Here is the rest of the advertisement:

"*Environmental Biology Program*. Study of the effects of outer space and planetary environments on living systems and processes, as conducted in ground-based laboratories and in outer space on space-flight missions. The ground-based studies are concerned with activity of earth organisms in simulated planetary environments, and terrestrial studies of ecological niches which offer extreme or unusual conditions. In-flight experiments concerned with biological aspects of the organism where exposed to weightlessness, space radiation, and the hard vacuum of space.

"*Behavioral Biology Program*. Studies concerning the biological bases of behavior, such as the investigation of behavioral pattern formation and localization at the cellular and subcellular (e.g., molecular) level, the application of cybernetics principles for the monitoring of the organism, including communication, orientation, and rhythmicity. Investigation of sensory and motor processes, vigilance, learning, thought, memory, and emotion, as they pertain to man's functioning in the space environment.

"*Physical Biology*. Study of the fundamental bases of performance including physiology of the respiratory system, cardiovascular system, and the central nervous system, as well as studies of metabolism and nutrition, and biomechanics (e.g., vibration, acceleration, and weightlessness). Also included are the blending of the disciplines of biology and physics in the production of instruments for biophysical observation and the acquisition of new biophysical data."

That more or less covers the waterfront. It includes exobiology, which goodness knows is inclusive enough, and it includes most of human biology and a great deal else. It leaves out the study of human reproduction and the density of populations. I suppose we are not quite ready to think of exporting the population en masse, or trips so long that human fertility and gestation become a problem. At least not in the NASA. It doesn't mention studies of the ocean floor, but that must have been an oversight. As far as this country is concerned it looks as though nearly the whole of biological science is being taken over, for where the money goes, biologists, like other sheep, are sure to follow. This might be all to the good, for it tends to put biology on the scientific throne as the successor to those more exact and fussy physical and chemical sciences that have sat there too long. The danger is that what NASA pays for, it will keep up its sleeve as hush-hush science withdrawn from the public domain where it belongs. And there is danger that the gossamer web of silver may tangle and trap the heretics and mavericks among the young biologists who might otherwise have seen new lights. Who pays the piper, calls the tune.

Anyway, who or what is man that he should want to venture beyond the Earth into the outer void? Here is the blind spot of science that looks upon the universe and all that is in it as though seeing it from the outside, as though the scientist were God looking upon His handiwork. This of course is a failing of the human being, not of the scientist as such. What is left out is the man and the scientist himself, for when an astronomer looks at a planet or a galaxy through a telescope we tend to forget that the telescope has two ends and that the eye and mind of the human being at one end may signify as much or more than all that is visible at the other. So when we put man into space, who is putting what into space and why?

Man of course is a backboned animal, whatever else he thinks he is, and there are many other such creatures. In the beginning all backboned animals were fish of a sort, swimming, respiring, and happily reproducing below the surface of the salt or fresh waters of the Earth. Man is also a tetrapod, a fellow member of the four-footed, land-plodding community that has descended from enterprising or scared fishlike creatures that progressively abandoned the restful, all-supporting medium of water for a life of lifting the body off the ground against the whole pull of gravity, surrounded only by insubstantial air. This passage from water to air was a necessary step along our path of destiny, and has much in common with what we are now aspiring to do.

When our fishy ancestors left their all-wet environment, where they had moved about by wagging their tails, and took up an exo-aquatic biological existence, thereafter to pick up one foot after another on land, they had to do far more than make the transit and acquire systems of bony levers and muscle straps for jerking their bodies along. They had to take with them the old wet and salty environment of the ancient seas, incorporated in their body fluids. The cells and tissues which constituted their being could no more survive out of water, and salt water at that, than they could survive unprotected on the face of the Moon. Only animals with water containing the old sea salts, bottled up inside the body, sealed in by an impervious outer skin, could stay alive in the new world out of water.

We and all the other descendants of these emancipated creatures are still essentially fish out of water, no matter how we may have changed our shapes. As such we have become further emancipated in important ways. Whether the world outside is hot or cold, we keep our body at a constant temperature, or die in the attempt, and we bear our young alive rather than lay old-fashioned eggs. So of course do pigs, and pigs have yet to fly.

More, therefore, has gone into the project. The ancestors of man have had an arboreal phase of existence which made the all-but-final changes in preparation for venturing into space. These consisted of transforming feet into hands in order to climb and swing among the trees and grasp any near objects that attracted attention; of putting distance between the nose and the telltale ground, thereby affording release from the enslaving sense of smell that holds most of the order of mammals in thrall; and of emphasizing sight, particularly the acquisition of binocular vision and with it the three-dimensional sense of space and distance. We have the eye-hand brain of the anthropoid, exceptionally well developed but none-the-less anthropoid. So we make the chimp lead the way into space, a monkey's paw in place of a cat's. True, we no longer watch the Moon from the tree-tops and we have reconverted our hind pair of anthropoid hands into running feet with a tendency to falling arches. But we see, hear, and think with a brain of a particular kind, accompanied by mischievous fingers and itching feet, with more real biological or living time, as distinct from calendar time, allotted to the span of life than is given to any other creature. It looks like trouble all the way.

So here we are, standing on our two hind legs, nose in the air, looking to the heavens and reaching for the stars. We have mastered the air, though later than the birds by more than a hundred million years, and we have put men into parking orbits around the Earth under conditions very close to outer space itself. Yet the rule still holds. Man, the bottled-up perambulating fish with sea salt still in his veins but air in his lungs, able to maintain himself comfortably only at the temperature and pressure that are standard at the surface of the Earth, can take off for more distant parts only if he bottles up the essence of the environment he has been born into. Sealed in plastic he takes on another skin,

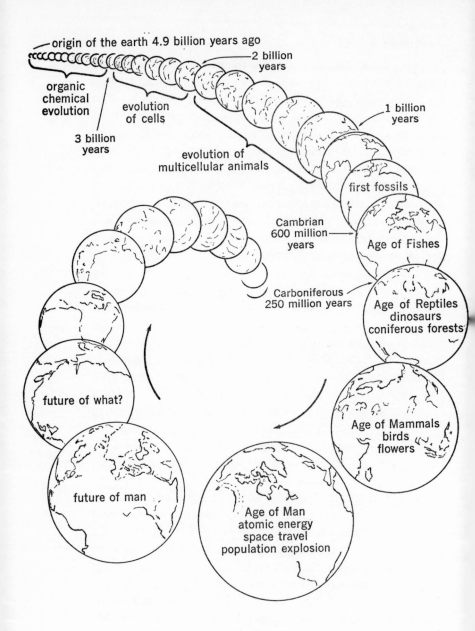

origin of the earth 4.9 billion years ago

2 billion years

organic chemical evolution

evolution of cells

3 billion years

1 billion years

evolution of multicellular animals

first fossils

Cambrian 600 million years

Age of Fishes

Carboniferous 250 million years

Age of Reptiles dinosaurs coniferous forests

future of what?

Age of Mammals birds flowers

future of man

Age of Man atomic energy space travel population explosion

Time Scale

with his terrestrial aerial environment between that and his living skin, and his old saltwater environment still flowing among his cells and tissues.

Emancipation from water called for drastic changes, in respiration and in coping with the force of gravity. Emancipation from air and gravity makes no less a demand. Man the organism can live in space only by assuming another guise which becomes essentially part of himself while in space, even though he can shed his new shape and skin on return to Earth. Adaptations, however, can go too far.

Man-in-Space is man out of bounds, there is no question of it. Not in the sense of trespassing, for no one else belongs there, but by way of edging closer to the furnace of life's forebeing. We lose more protection than we are aware of when we leave the atmosphere behind. Landing on other planets is another matter. Climatically they are bound to be hostile to the Earth-born, though if not so poorly made or placed as to be barren they will be home to whatever they have evolved, in which case we certainly will be trespassing and at our own risk.

Putting first things first, however, the problems of space travel are twofold, quite apart from those of propulsion and navigation. These are fundamentally the same problems any creature has to face—how to live inside its skin and how to defend itself from the external and always somewhat hostile world in which it finds itself. That is to say, how to keep a man alive for an extended period within a sealed capsule, without regard to what may lie outside the capsule, and how to protect the man inside the capsule from the hostility of what lies without—the cosmic vacuum, unfiltered solar radiation, cosmic rays, and the shattering debris of the solar system. Both are interesting exercises in ingenuity, to say the least.

Man in a capsule is like a goldfish in a bowl that is glass

all over, with no air space. Nothing can be added to what is already there, nothing can truly be subtracted because there is no place for it to go. The goldfish's life would be short and not so merry—all that was needed would soon be used up and all that was produced as waste would accumulate as poison. Life can continue in such a closed system only so long as a complete recycling process is possible. For short trips, such as those already accomplished by orbiting astronauts or those required to reach the Moon, the problems of creature intake and output have already been fairly well solved. For a round-trip to Mars, which would take about three years including the stopover necessary to get close enough to the Earth for the return take-off, the question of maintenance becomes far more difficult.

In fact we need to remember in all this talk of traveling in space, of landing on and possibly colonizing other planets, and of perhaps finding strange forms of indigenous life on some of the planets, that organisms are organisms whether they have assumed the shape of man or microbe or some alien form we know not of. And organisms are delicate, fragile forms of organized matter that are readily recognized but are by no means easy to comprehend or even define in a meaningful way. The vital thing about any organism, whether it be butterfly or daisy or fungus or girl, is that it is something that happens and not merely something that is. Like the stream of consciousness itself, the whole organism, whether a conscious kind or not, is truly a streaming in of unorganized and relatively simple raw materials which take their place momentarily in an infinitely complex, organized, living machinery and displace what had shortly gone before them—as though new bricks were popping into place in a falling-down brick house as fast as old bricks were slipping out of place. This is so whether we are considering a single-cell or a multibillion-cell creature.

Any serious interruption of input of any kind or blocking of output quickly leads to death and destruction. Hence the tremendous emphasis already being given to the so-called biological engineering problems of space travel, for the conditions of space travel under the circumstances must include the period of any planetary visit in addition to transit time.

Accordingly, much has been said about a system of conjugal life called symbiosis, although the word may not be common currency in the jargon of space biology. Certain rather simple forms of life, lowdown but lovely, such as corals and some South Sea Island clams, contain within their tissues innumerable single-cell plants living in the most intimate association it is possible to imagine. The unicellular plants are of a kind that live freely and abundantly in the oceans and are generally responsible for the starlight phosphorescence of the seas on dark nights. Those within the cells of animals interlock their metabolism with that of their hosts. The plants flourish by utilizing the waste, ammonia and carbon dioxide especially, of the host tissues and at the same time give off free oxygen as a by-product of their photosynthesis, which is an aid to the internal respiration of the animal tissue, and throw in some carbohydrates for good measure. In fact a good time is had by all, although the mutual satisfaction may not be equal.

So plans and experiments proceed to devise systems within plastic space capsules where a similar kind of plant life liberates free oxygen and combines with carbon dioxide and other substances. Such is the principle of the thing—a plant-animal metabolic system where everything goes round and round. Simply to produce enough oxygen, however, the plants, whether microscopic algae, duckweed, or celery cabbage, would have to have a total leaf surface of more than fifteen square yards—an appallingly large amount of salad for one man to take along. Of course no one needs to go out into space to develop this particular part of the program. It is only when we begin to call our long shots that space travel becomes a grim business of touch and go, or, more likely, be touched and be gone.

The hazards of space outside the capsule are formidable. It is not merely the vacuum without. That is different only in degree from what lies outside a high-flying airplane. The great difference, apart from pressure and air to breathe, is radiation. Here at sea level we and all other life live at the bottom of an ocean of air. In equivalent weight this overhead mass of air amounts to thirty feet of water, and that is a barrier of no mean dimension. It acts not only as a barrier but as a filter and modifier of the savage thrust of solar and cosmic radiation. We are shielded from the harshness of the universe, though not entirely.

The solar light that penetrates the atmosphere and appears to us as white light, occasionally seen refracted in full panoply as a rainbow, includes light invisible to the human eye. At one end is the infra-red, sensed by some creatures, if not by us; and at the other the black light, or ultraviolet, clearly seen by bees and such. Though we see it not, we tan under its influence, while many less-skin-protected creatures, particularly those shielded by living in water, are soon killed when exposed to the ultraviolet rays. Yet these are merely the softer rays marginal to visible blue light itself. The really lethal, shortwave, ultraviolet is stopped in its tracks high in the atmosphere by oxygen. The high-altitude oxygen molecules absorb the ultraviolet energy, and are transformed into a belt of ozone in the process. Without that belt, life on Earth might never have emerged from its watery cradle. Outside the ozone belt, however, even the most deadly ultraviolet is the most readily warded off of the radiation to be encountered.

First come the Van Allen belts, great belts of cosmic rays trapped within the Earth's magnetic fields and so intense as to completely overwhelm and blank out the Geiger counters carried aloft by early satellites into their region. The first belt begins about 500 miles up and extends to 2,500 miles; the second begins at about 12,000 and extends to more than 50,000 miles from the Earth. This is deadly stuff with the penetrating power of X-rays. Our orbiting astronauts are kept well below the lower ceiling, for continuous exposure in orbiting capsules would be as fatal as a beam of intense X-rays on an unprotected man. To get out into real space, the real start of a journey, would require tons of heavy shielding incompatible with all other requirements, or such a fast trip that astronauts would survive with nothing worse than sterilization or eventual cancer, unless an exit could be made directly out into space from one of the Earth's Poles, inside the circle of the Northern or Southern lights where the danger is minimal.

Once out and beyond, probably only solar flares are to be worried about, flares which are colossal upheavals through the Sun's surface, extending as masses of fiery gas as far as the Earth's orbit and beyond, and everywhere in between. The Earth's enveloping atmosphere shields the life below, but astronauts protected only by the thin skin of their space ship and its light bulwarks would be vulnerable indeed. Even periods such as the Year of the Quiet Sun are not to be trusted, and in any case would not be long enough to allow for a safe round-trip to Mars. The solution is yet to come.

Nor is this all. Expeditions that venture beyond Mars, into the belt of the solar system lying between the orbits of Mars and Jupiter, would run into planetary traffic as hazardous as a downtown city thoroughfare during a rush hour. This is the belt of the asteroids, where one or more planets appear to have shattered from collision or from some more obscure cause, to leave upward of 30,000 fragments large enough to be seen through telescopes on Earth, and goodness knows what infinitude of smaller pieces, flying around the Sun. Nor is the immediate neighborhood of the Earth any too safe, for the meteorites, large and small, that fall on the Earth and have bespeckled the Moon, are erratic strays from the same source. One clean hit or even a grazing one would eliminate a space ship without a trace.

Physical hazards are not the only kind. If a man should succeed in traversing the irradiated space vacuum between here and another planet, it is important that he arrive in a reasonably sane condition. Will he lose the regular 24-hour activity cycles of body and mind? Almost certainly, according to experiments already carried out on an individual kept in a soundproof, continuously lighted room for four months. For what it is worth, the subject showed increased irritability and a heightened artistic sense as time went on. Psychologically, however, there is an immense difference between being in space and being in a room which seems like being in space.

When all is said and done, and the environmental problems presented by travel in space have been satisfactorily resolved, the chief problem is a matter of time. A trip to Mars not only will require several months of travel time each way, but, because the Earth outpaces Mars in going round the Sun, an Earthling on Mars would have to wait for the Earth to come round again before the return journey could be made. The better part of two years would pass between leaving and re-entry. Sanity and sustenance—easy enough to maintain during the brief orbiting trips around the Earth—become precarious indeed when interplanetary travel by humans really gets started.

Orr Reynolds of NASA suggests that space travel of long duration may well require the development of a new interdisciplinary technology, to be known as gastronautics. It is all very well for those of us who sit on Earth and enjoy the running report of space feats to say that sending astronauts to the Moon or Mars is an exciting event. The Romans undoubtedly felt the same way about the gladiators and other hapless individuals playing the bloody game in the Coliseum arena. If we make these vicarious trips, which is all that but a very few can ever do, we should at least journey mentally with the traveler. A little empathy could go a long way. With the assurance that life in space is possible, the question is, therefore, what is going to make living in space worth while? Deprived of most of the elements of human society, the suggestion is that food might seem to offer a happy association with familiar experience and some small semblance of satisfaction.

Yet there's the rub: How to lift a two-year supply of steak and potato into space. Energy pills, so effective in science fiction, will stay in science fiction. Real food is essential, quite apart from keeping that contented look on the face of the astronaut. Even in the form of concentrated food pills, however, in order to meet the basic daily requirements, a man would have to swallow about 90 large-size capsules containing protein, minerals, and vitamins, and another 250 capsules of fat to furnish energy. Another suggestion has been that we should fatten the space traveler like a Strasbourg goose and make him live on his own fat. Out there he wouldn't even lose weight! Unfortunately, a semistarved astronaut would have so deteriorated in sense and senses that he would have been better left at home, for he would do nothing but dream of food were he

allowed to go. What *is* the answer? I doubt if anyone
knows, at least not yet. More food would require more lift,
especially at blast-off, and there are limits to both what is
possible and what is worth while. Perhaps there *is* no
answer.

F O U R

Martian Landing

MARS, THE RED PLANET and the God of War, can be seen only as the Earth turns its face from the Sun to look into the dark, outer, star-studded void of the night. For Mars moves in an orbit farther beyond the Earth than is Venus toward the Sun. If Venus can be called the twin but barren sister to the Earth, Mars is no more than a small cousin, half the Earth's diameter though twice that of the Moon, a slowpoke who takes two of our years to make its own unearthly round of the Sun. Yet the planet spins about its axis as rapidly as does the Earth, lively enough in its place.

Mars also has two moons. Kepler, in a letter to Galileo, assigned two moons to the planet more than three hundred years ago, before any had been seen and without known reason. Clairvoyance? In any case his statement became respected and we find a remarkably Keplerian account of them by Dean Swift a century later in *Gulliver's Travels,* ostensibly by Gulliver in the part called "A voyage to Laputa." This is a section modeled after "A voyage to Tonquin," part of the never-to-be-forgotten *A New Voyage Round the World,* by William Dampier, the pirate-naturalist who was a contemporary of Swift at the turn of the seventeenth century.

Referring to the astronomers of Laputa, Gulliver had this to say:

"They spend the greatest part of their lives in observing the celestial bodies, which they do by the assistance of glasses far excelling ours in goodness. For although their largest telescopes do not exceed three feet, they magnify much more than those of a hundred among us, and at the same time show the stars with greater clearness. This advantage hath enabled them to extend their discoveries much further than our astronomers in Europe. They have made a catalogue of ten thousand fixed stars, whereas the largest of ours do not contain above one third part of that number. They have likewise discovered two lesser stars, or satellites, which revolve about Mars; whereof the innermost is distant from the centre of the primary planet exactly three of the diameters, and the outermost five; the former revolves in the space of ten hours, and the latter in twenty-one and a half; so that the squares of their periodical times are very near in the same proportion with the cubes of their distance from the centre of Mars; which evidently shows them to be governed by the same law of gravitation, that influences the other heavenly bodies."

The last part of this is a straight statement of Kepler's third law of planetary motion, namely, that the square of a planet's period is proportional to the cube of the semi-major axis (which in the case of circular orbits is the radius from the Sun's center to that of the planet). Dean Swift, substituting the planet and its moons for the sun and its planets, one satellite system for another, evidently employed Kepler's law to calculate the periods of satellite moons in orbits close to the surface of a planet. That was elementary mathematics, certainly, but remember no one had seen any Martian moons, let alone their rate of revolution or distance from the planet. Only the moons of Jupiter, first seen by Galileo, were known.

The moons of Mars were actually observed first by Asaph Hall, an American astronomer, in 1877, who named them Phobos and Deimos, meaning fear and panic, fitting attendants to the God of War. They are small, no more than a few miles across, and travel fast. Believe it or not, Phobos, the inner moon, lies two diameters of the planet distant from the center and makes the round in seven and a half hours. It is only fitting that the first American probe to be sent to Mars is named after Gulliver.

The Martian moons are by no means the kind to set your lunar rhythms by, and they have been called astronomical impossibilities that could never have been formed at the time the planet itself was made. Some Russians consider them to be little more than hollow shells and the suggestion has been made, seriously or otherwise, that they are artificial satellites, a final gesture of a civilization about to perish. Such a thought is at least in keeping with the belief in Martian canals, dug and operated by Martian engineers. We do seem to project both our dreams and our nightmares into the heavens.

The canals, so-called, were discovered by the Italian astronomer Giovanni Schiaparelli, also in the year 1877, while he was mapping out the deserts and darker regions of Mars. Just for a moment, when the Earth's atmosphere ceased its infernal dance and the image cleared, he saw a network of faint lines crossing the deserts, and caught further glimpses of them during the night. He called them *canali*, intending to mean natural channels rather than man-made canals, though the latter meaning was taken when his account was translated into English. Two years later when Mars was again in opposition he reported that some of the canals had doubled, a discovery somewhat disconcerting to those who would have preferred to believe that intelligent beings had dug them.

This might have been the end of them had it not been for one the Boston Brahmins, Dr. Percival Lowell, a man of many interests and many moods, financially independent, well trained in mathematics and physics but not a professional astronomer. The canals of Mars caught his imagination and he built an observatory at Flagstaff, Arizona, to study them. He was sure he could see canals, and drew elaborate maps of their courses; he was convinced that they had been constructed by intelligent people to conserve a dwindling water supply. His ideas, presented enthusiastically in lectures and books, evoked headlines in newspapers and worldwide discussion, so much so that the discovery of anything less on Mars may seem an anticlimax. No lines suggestive of canals have yet been photographed, although it is still true that when conditions are good the human eye can see the surface of Mars more clearly through the Earth's atmosphere than can any camera.

Even when it was pointed out that to be seen at all the canals must be twenty to thirty miles wide, and when he was asked why some of the canals were double, Lowell said that what we actually were looking at was a wide belt of vegetation at each side of a narrow irrigating canal and that the second canal was used to return the irrigation water to the polar snow caps from which it came, with pumping stations all along the route. It still is an appealing picture, for, no matter what Martians may have looked like, projects such as these are so much a product of a human-type brain that we have a fellow feeling and would welcome the companionship it could imply. Displaced from the center of creation, we already sense our isolation and feel a little lonely. Unfortunately, wishful thinking has none of the impact of a Creator's original thought and leaves a planet —any planet—with no more and no less than such life as the planet has been able to evolve from its solar system dust in the course of its time. So, with our feet a little more firmly fixed on Earth and our heads not quite so much in the clouds, what can we truly expect of Mars, particularly in the aftermath of disappointment over Venus?

First, a few vital statistics, particularly concerning temperature and atmosphere, the two features of greatest significance with regard to the presence or absence of life. The temperature is variable, not only between day and night and between the equator and the poles, but from one season to another. For Mars spins about a tilted axis, just like the Earth, and has also an elliptical orbit. The planet is closest to the Sun when the south pole is tilted toward the Sun, and so summer is warmest and winter is coldest in the southern hemisphere.

Because of its greater distance from the Sun, Mars receives less than half the light intensity reaching the Earth. It is also cooler, both because of the distance and because the relatively lightweight planet holds a much thinner atmosphere which allows a greater amount of heat to escape at night. Daily temperature variation is as great as that of the Gobi Desert, with the mid-day temperature at the equator rising to about 86° F. and falling at night to well below −100° F. This is a decidedly rigorous environment in terms of temperature alone. And for Earthlings the atmospheric pressure would be another discomforting feature, for it is but one tenth of the atmospheric pressure at Earth ground level, and no more than would be encountered at twice the height of Mount Everest. One tenth normal atmospheric pressure means getting dangerously close to the level at which human blood would boil at the temperature of the human body.

So far no oxygen has been detected spectrographically in the Martian atmosphere. Carbon dioxide is present, probably in a concentration about ten times as high as in the atmosphere of the Earth. The bulk of the atmosphere is thought to be nitrogen, as it is here. Apart from lack of oxygen and low pressure, both negative features, the atmosphere of Mars does not appear to be actively hostile as in the case of Venus. Which leaves the question of water vapor and the presence of liquid water.

The two most striking aspects of Mars as seen through even small Earth-based telescopes are the white polar caps and the dark and orange areas that lie between, both of which undergo very marked seasonal change. Earlier observers regarded the polar caps as snowfields similar to those of Earth, and watched them shrink steadily during the spring of the hemisphere concerned; during the following summer they become very small, and sometimes the southern cap disappears completely for a while. Later on some astronomers suggested that the white caps might be 'dry ice,' or frozen carbon dioxide, but spectroscopic methods have definitely shown them to be frozen water in some form—snow, ice, or hoarfrost. Moreover, traces of water vapor have recently been detected in the atmosphere. What appears certain, however, is that the polar caps are less than a foot deep and cannot be truly likened to those of the Earth. And the extreme shrinkage they undergo in their respective spring seasons may not be a melting to liquid water but a sublimation directly into water vapor.

The dark patches on Mars have been under close observation during the last three centuries. Their general outlines seem to be more or less permanent, and detailed surface maps have been drawn at various times, all in good agreement except the more fanciful pictures of Lowell. These areas also undergo regular changes in color with the changing seasons. As the polar caps shrink with the warmer weather, the adjacent dark patches become darker, and sharper, as though affected by the arrival of moisture. Often the colors become brownish, reddish, black, or even a moss green. Elsewhere the planet surface appears reddish and generally dusty, suggesting desert conditions.

It is very significant that the color change begins in spring next to the polar cap and progresses toward the equator, indicating a close dependence of the color change upon the melting of the polar cap. During the spring of the southern hemisphere the color change continues over the equator into the northern hemisphere. Occasionally new areas appear, or well-known ones vanish and reappear. An area known as Hellas, for instance, darkened in 1954 but was bright again in 1956, and another dark area about the size of Texas appeared in what had before been open desert. The natural explanation would seem to be that the areas which darken with the apparent spread of moisture represent vegetation of some sort, although non-living, chemical changes have also been suggested.

Perhaps the crucial question relating to Mars as a possible abode of life concerns not so much whether water is present, for that seems certain, but how much water is there. Estimations of the water vapor in the atmosphere made from the observatory at the top of the Jungfrau and more or less confirmed by observations from high-altitude balloons, indicate that there is barely enough to cover the surface of Mars with a film of moisture. This suggests that the extent of free water evaporating at the surface is not great, but it says nothing of the possibility of ice. One Russian astronomer believes that the so-called canals may actually be great fissures in a thick layer of ice covering the planet.

On the assumption that Mars has proportionately as much water at its surface as the Earth, he reckons that the Martian oceans, considering the prevailing temperatures, are covered with a layer of ice nearly 1,000 feet thick at the equator and about 6,000 feet thick at the poles. Why, then, doesn't the planet appear as a solid ball of ice? Because it most likely has been covered with sand and dust during the past hundreds of millions of years. Earthquakes—or quakes, anyway—have produced fissures in the ice that have exposed the ground below, and it is in these exposed areas that Martian vegetation has been primarily concentrated. Surprises undoubtedly await us on Mars, but it is doubtful that this will be one of them. At the same time, if the spin of a planet has anything to do with the extrusion of water at the surface, which seems to be the case with the Earth, the rapid spin of Mars may be indicative. What we need now is not further speculation on the meaning of the known facts, but more facts to speculate on.

Mars has somewhat suddenly become tremendously important to mankind, both from the point of view of scientists, especially biologists, and to man as a whole in relation to his view of the universe and his place within it. Before the Renaissance the Earth and Man were the center of the universe, the apple of God's eye, and all was well. With the dethronement brought about by Copernicus, Brahe, Kepler, and Galileo, the Earth was displaced from the center of all things to the status of a middle-sized planet circling a middle-sized sun somewhere in an outer, dusty arm of one of uncountable galaxies. This raises sharply the question of the origination of life on Earth, whether it has been a freak happening on what seems to be an incidental planet, with the consequent likelihood that life and man

are unique and of little significance, or whether life origi-
nates on any planet suitably made and suitably placed relative to its sun, with the implication that life may be as
significant in the universe as the stars themselves. If life has
arisen here as the natural outcome of the early conditions
of the Earth, as we now think, then proof of this is greatly
needed if we are to feel safe in building our new concept
of the nature of things. The step-by-step reconstruction in
the laboratory of how life could have arisen, in terms of
chemistry, will of course be substantial circumstantial evidence that life did so arise. Much progress along this line
has already been made.

The real proof, however, would be the discovery of life
on other planets, for then we would at least know that we,
the life of the Earth, are not the only interesting planetary
scum in creation. Even the lowliest form of life on even the
most miserable of possible planets would be proof enough,
no matter how disappointing in other respects. So far as
this solar system is concerned, now that expectation of finding indigenous life on the Moon has faded and our anticipation of finding Venus suitable for life has been dashed,
Mars remains our only hope. The others—Mercury close
to the Sun and the large outer planets too far from the Sun
—have never been seriously considered in this respect.

Taken altogether, the evidence makes the existence of
life on Mars almost a certainty. To obtain the proof and
to find out more about such life requires the sending of instruments to Mars which could report and possibly bring
back data and samples, to be followed by manned flights
capable of much more elaborate procedures. Either way it
is desirable to have at least some inkling of what to expect.

To begin with, the nature of Martian organisms must
be able to account for a number of the planetary features
already observed. They must be visible or must form visi-

ble colonies which cover the ground rather extensively.
They must account for the color and the observed color
changes. They must account for the changes in size and
shape of the Martian areas, must be able to migrate and
grow with some rapidity and able to re-emerge from a
covering of yellow dust. Such organisms must be able to
do this in an extremely thin atmosphere containing a good
deal of carbon dioxide but only traces of oxygen or water
and occasional ultraviolet light. And they must conform to
certain rules of life, particularly with regard to the recycling of the elements, that is, the old familiar business
of dust to dust.

We should remember, too, that on Earth organisms can
and do live in some amazing places. Bacteria grow and
multiply in the sands of the desert and high in the atmosphere. Some algae live in hot springs or in mountain snow
banks. Other organisms thrive in vinegar, in tanks of gaso-
line and phenol, and in the dark cold of the oceanic abyss.
None of them could account for what we can see on Mars.
Nor could any form of animal life, although some kind of
animal-like life may be present feeding on the more vegetative sort. Lichens have been suggested as the type of
vegetation we could expect to find, but lichens themselves
are a combination of fungus and alga and, although tough
and often content with a minimum of oxygen and water,
are so slow-growing as to be put out of court. A lichen
patch over-grazed by caribou may take twenty-five years to
recover, a far cry from the seasonal reappearance of apparent vegetation on Mars extending over hundreds of miles.

What about intelligence? If plantlike organisms have
solved the problems of growth on Mars, more active things,
like animals, may have evolved as well and, if so, they may
have reached the status of intelligence. Under the prevailing circumstances this seems unlikely. Certainly our plans

are being laid with minimal assumptions. On the other hand it would be more than interesting in both directions if we landed animated instruments in Martian backyards.

So the time has come for "Gulliver," the actual quest for life on Mars. In brief this is a project to land devices on Mars by parachute from a satellite put into Martian orbit from the Earth. One such device is designed to shoot out two weights with sticky strings upon arrival at the surface. The strings will then be wound back into a chamber containing a special broth in which it is hoped that any captured microörganisms might multiply. A detection system would analyze gases thereby produced and would radio the results back to Earth. As a Russian delegate to an international committee discussing this matter asked, does not the proposed experiment assume that Martian bacteria would have the same taste in broth as terrestrial ones? Efforts are therefore now being made to devise experiments which would reveal the existence of exotic forms of life—that is, to imagine forms of miscrscopic life with which we are totally unfamiliar and then to devise experiments to detect their presence, which is a stimulating mental exercise, to say the least.

This is merely the beginning. As the director of the NASA Bioscience Programs has said:

"The search for life on Mars ultimately will require that Martian samples be studied in manned (preferably terrestrial) laboratories. Many of us believe that the retrieval of Martian samples should be recognized explicitly as the ultimate objective of exobiological missions. It is doubtful if such retrieval can be accomplished satisfactorily by an unmanned expedition. . . . Not since Darwin, and Copernicus before him, has science had the opportunity for so great an impact on man's understanding of man. The scientific question at stake in exobiology is, in the opinion of many, the most exciting, challenging, and profound issue not only of the century but of the whole naturalistic movement that has characterized the history of western thought for 300 years. What is at stake is the chance to gain a wholly new level of discussion on the meaning and nature of life."

The finding of any form of life on Mars will set the stage, and analysis of even the simplest forms could supply us with information of inestimable value. This may be the one and only opportunity we can ever have to make a direct comparison of the basic nature of the living protoplasm typical of one planet with that of another. Analysis of Martian life accordingly represents a grand extension of the comparative method characteristic of most biological analysis. For example, shall we find on Mars some of the unexplained peculiarities of terrestrial biology? Is the energy-transfer system of living substance based on phosphorus, as it is here? What is the genetic mechanism for transmitting inheritance from generation to generation? What are the replication and information systems involved in growth, development, and reproduction? Is there sex? What evolutionary mechanisms operate? How are organisms adapted to the thin atmosphere, low oxygen, and Martian temperature range? And what evidence is there of a fossilized Martian past? With answers in hand to all of this, our understanding and appreciation of the nature of Earthly life will have taken a tremendous step forward, and in a way that we cannot otherwise accomplish. Kepler wished to get to the Moon primarily to see the Earth revolving in perspective. Our wish to get to Mars is comparable, but with regard to Earthly life rather than to the planet as a celestial body.

The stake is enormous and on no account must the chance be fumbled. If we are careless and by mischance establish on Mars microörganisms of Earthly origin before we know all we need to know about what is truly Martian, our one chance may have gone for good. The sterilization of interplanetary vehicles is therefore a major concern.

Sterility is by no means achieved simply by passage through interplanetary space. Neither vacuum nor extremely low temperatures have any harmful effects on any microörganisms so far tested. The fact that bacteria have survived imprisonment in Antarctic ice for nearly half a century, since the Shackleton expedition of 1917, is indicative of their hardiness. And the discovery that a number of bacterial strains have been recovered alive from ancient salt deposits of 180 and 320 million years ago is startling indeed. Complete sterilization of interplanetary vehicles is consequently something which has to be considered even during the designing stage and must be accomplished step by step during assembly to be effective. This is routine for the packaged instruments we are already sending into space. The greater difficulty comes when manned vehicles are sent abroad. The problem is so great that it is fortunate we—or our delegates—are not yet ready to go and may not go for years to come. Space ships may be sterilized, but not space travelers, human or otherwise. The healthiest human being is a hive of viruses, bacteria, and protozoans, some of which are essential to health itself. Others live happily within us whether we like them or not. It is vital that the space traveler who lands on Mars or elsewhere be as completely sealed off from the strange planet as a chick is inside its shell. Otherwise a planetwide situation could develop comparable to the virtual extermination of South Pacific islanders in the nineteenth century by measles, whooping cough, and other diseases relatively harmless to white men.

And by the same token, anything brought back alive could be dangerous to our own existence. Any visit to Mars must therefore be made with extreme circumspection for, as already demonstrated here on Earth, man appears to be a menace to all that attracts him. The longer it takes the blacksmiths of manned space travel to perfect their hardware, the better pleased the biologists will be.

Out from the Sun

THESE ARE HEADY TIMES. Curiosity has led us to analyzing atoms, cells, and stars. A sense of power, which is something else, leads us to blow atoms apart on a genocidal scale, to hurl missiles at the Moon, and to try our hand at creating life. In a portentous way it is all fun and games, for the rule seems to be, what man can do he will do and should do. Those whom the gods love they first drive mad. We seem to be committed.

In the beginning all was dark. Then light came. Such was the intuition or inspiration of earlier men. We now agree with them, and somehow admire ourselves in so doing. For the modern view is that the solar system condensed from a slowly turning disc-shaped cloud of cold interstellar dust, itself a product of exploded stars. This separated into a large central revolving mass and a thin, extensive outer disc. As the center continued to condense it developed heat and became the incandescent Sun. The peripheral disc eddied into smaller planetary accumulations of the cosmic dust, all moving around the Sun and each with a spin of its own. Thus arose the solar system, five billion years ago, with the planets spaced in orderly precession of orbits, from Mercury's at 36 million to Pluto's at 3,600 million miles outward from the Sun.

Again at the beginning, Earth and the other inner proto-planets were probably a thousand times as great in weight and diameter as they now are, comparable in size to the outer planets as they are at present. The proto-Earth would have been about 80,000 miles across, a whirling cloud of ice particles and solid fragments, with the heavier fragments sinking toward the center. Then followed a slimming process whereby this planet and its closest neighbors lost their lighter, outer envelopes of water molecules, hydrogen, and other gases, under the impact of the young Sun in all its power and majesty. Solar heat broke up the atmospheric substances, and pressure of light drove them outward into space. Thus Mercury, Venus, Earth, and Mars lost all or most of their original mantles and broiled or basked in the radiance of the Sun.

Farther out, beyond the orbit of fragmented asteroids, the giant planets—Jupiter, Saturn, Uranus, and Neptune —too far from the Sun to be so affected, have held on to their birthright, unchanging through the course of time. Little Pluto, apparently a stray beyond recall, circles around the lot.

Such is the setting—a solar furnace grown from a cold beginning, and a scattering of planets spun out toward the night. The whole persists in a spinning state, like an enormous revolving stage with the planetary actors pirouetting within it. The Sun itself, close to a million miles in diameter, turns about its axis in roughly twenty-seven days. Mercury and Venus, closest to the Sun, have yielded such spin as they may have had. Earth and Mars both take the twenty-four hours we call our day, but may have spun faster in the past. The giants all spin faster, in ten hours

more or less. And all make their stately round of the Sun—
an 88-day circuit for Mercury, 365 days for Earth, 687 days
for Mars, about 12 years for Jupiter, 30 for Saturn, the
span of a man's life for Uranus and twice that for Neptune.
And all but Mercury and Venus are moon-encircled. This
is the system in which life has arisen—on Earth as we
know, on Mars most likely, but elsewhere with hardly a
chance.

All Earthly life is very watery—98 per cent for a jellyfish, 68 per cent for the whole man and much higher than
that if the bones are omitted. Water makes up the bulk of
all living substance, though arranged in curiously fluid
crystalline form within the matrix of other matter. And
living cells, unless well fortified, live bathed in aqueous
salt solutions either in the body or of the outside world.
The water of protoplasm is as much a part of the living
substance as the proteins themselves, and as hard to squeeze
out as is water from cheese. Yet it flows, not merely as a
semiliquid in the structure of cells, but in the same sense
as all other components of life, as a steady replacement of
water already architecturally incorporated.

We do not know and have not yet conceived how the
familiar qualities of life can be expressed in the absence
of water in its liquid state. On these terms life seems possible only within the temperature range between steam
and ice, which puts a crimp on planetary possibilities
within this or any other solar system. Too near the Sun
water exists as superheated steam, and too readily escapes
into space. Too far from the Sun it persists as crystalline
ice. Only in a relatively narrow belt at some distance from
the Sun can water be water with all its uniqueness and
liquidity. Such a belt will itself have an inner and outer
region, where liquid water barely makes the grade, with a
happy mean in between. Venus lies apparently just over

the inner edge, in the overheated zone, Mars just inside the outer edge, with no more than minimal subsistence. Only Earth lies where a planet needs to be for water to be the mother of life in all its varied panoply.

If the watery surface of the Earth became alive as a natural course in the development of the planet, rather than as seeds from space or as an afterthought of an indefinable and capricious Creator, when and how did it happen? Under present circumstances any half-living stuff would be taken apart and be consumed by bacteria as fast as it came into being, and no new life could get going. The beginning must lie so far back in time that all was sterile, other than the primordial stirring, when even bacteria were a monumental advance in the future. All the evidence from fossilized forms of life and of life's chemical products incorporated in the rocks push the origin far into the infancy of the Earth itself. So somewhere in that murky stretch of time between three and four billion years ago, when protoplanets had already assumed their planetary distinction, matter at the surface of the Earth became a little more lively than before.

How this liveliness came to be was a stumbling block to scientists for many years—the gulf between the non-living and the living seemed unbridgeable and a mysterious life-spark was evoked. The first cell was considered a miracle, and the organic compounds that composed it were things apart from the inorganic world. All this has now changed. The transformation of simple inorganic substances into some of the most significant constituents of living cells is a new and still exciting human accomplishment. Having failed to see how God could have done it, we have managed to do it ourselves—an inflationary step for the human ego.

The important insight came from a comparative study of the atmospheres of the planets by the atomic chemist

H. E. Urey, then at the University of Chicago. Why was the atmosphere of the Earth—mainly molecular nitrogen, very rich in oxygen, but poor in carbon dioxide—so different from the others? Why were the others so rich in the reducing gases such as ammonia, methane, and carbon monoxide? Part of the answer comes from the processes of vegetative life. Photosynthesis in green plants involves splitting water molecules into hydrogen and oxygen, and combining the hydrogen with carbon dioxide to form carbohydrates. Carbon dioxide is removed from the atmosphere or from solution in water, and oxygen for the most part is liberated as an unwanted byproduct into the atmosphere. Were it not for this activity, all the free oxygen in the atmosphere would disappear in a few thousand years by combining with various substances in the Earth's surface, and carbon dioxide would accumulate in non-living form.

This being so, the thought arises—what sort of atmosphere did the Earth have before green plant life evolved, that is, before oxygen was poured into the atmosphere and carbon dioxide withdrawn? The answer, simply put, is that it was not an oxidizing atmosphere as it is now but was a reducing one, like those of the outer planets particularly. From this point of view the outer planets are museum pieces, with their original atmospheres preserved by the deep cold that lies beyond the effective reach of the Sun. The next step in thinking was—what happened on Earth that led to the emergence of life and the change in atmospheric constitution? Here matters begin to get technical, for the chemistry of life is by far the most complex we know.

To start with, the Earth not only would have had a reducing atmosphere, with hydrogen compounds of nitrogen and carbon predominating, together with hydrogen itself to some extent and at least some carbon dioxide and water

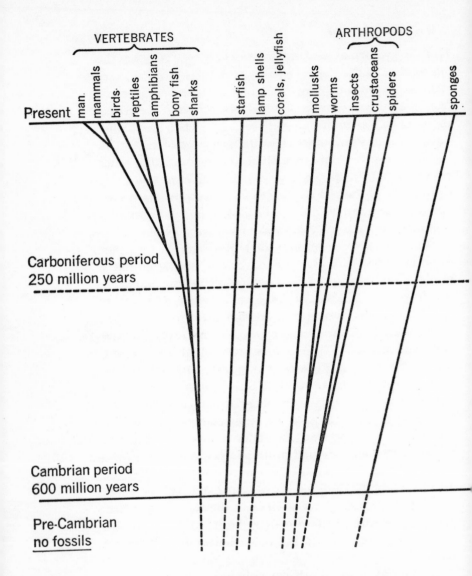

The "Bush of Life"

The fossil record opens with the major lines already established at the beginning of the Cambrian period. The first sign of vertebrates is even later, although they must have existed earlier.

vapor, but the Sun's ultraviolet radiation would have driven unchecked to the surface of the Earth, to an extent life could not at present tolerate. Before the atmosphere became rich in oxygen, there could be no absorption of ultraviolet to form the high-level protective ozone belt, and the driving energy of the shortwave light came all the way.

When light of this sort, or similar to it, drives in among a mixture of gases such as those of a primitive atmosphere, what happens? Put to the test, the answer comes fast and clear. These very simple but mostly toxic gases combine with one another to form carbohydrates, fatty acids, and amino acids, the very building blocks of living matter, ordinarily produced during photosynthesis and made use of by all plant and animal life on Earth. Other, more intricate, but increasingly important chemical components of living cells have been produced in laboratories under somewhat more complex and different circumstances, and all doubt has vanished that such has been the general course of the origination of living things—step by step, interacting all the time, in a veritable primordial salty soup of organic compounds, driven remorselessly together by the unfiltered light of the Sun.

Eventually, perhaps after a billion years of such goings-on, units of matter, with matter streaming in and out, became so organized and large as to be recognizable as cells, some as bacteria and some as more complex cells equipped with internal photosynthetic structures. With this accomplished, things began to clear up. As life became more and more concentrated in the forms of free, independent but self-enclosed cells, the organic soupiness of the original seas slowly cleared and the cells as organisms progressively had to compete for the materials that lay without. And as organized photosynthesis within the cells took over the business of making the building blocks of protoplasm, the atmosphere, and the water exposed to it, became steadily richer in oxygen, thereby setting the stage for the more mobile but less independent kind of life we know and experience in ourselves as animal. There was time enough for all this too, maybe another billion years from the Earth's beginning, so much time went by before anything more than fossilized cells appeared in the record of the rocks.

The Earth, then, as we now find her, is a middle-aged planet with much, if not most, of her destiny already fulfilled. Her original atmospheric mantle was transformed while life was still a multitudinous microbial world. The great pageant of evolutionary creation came very much later, during periods of continental and oceanic growth. The seas, in fact, have deepened throughout geological time, as water has squeezed to the surface through the interstices of the crust. Planets that bear life not only have to be born but must be made and remade with passing time, if Mother Earth is anything to go by.

Beyond the water belt of the solar system the outer planets are lively enough, even though lifeless. The greatest is Jupiter, named after the omnipotent god, and the first intact planet beyond Mars, more than three hundred times as massive as the Earth, sufficient even to disturb the motion of the Sun. According to Kepler's rule of location of planets, a planet should exist between Mars and Jupiter, but it is not to be seen in planetary form. This is the zone of the asteroids, 1,600 of which are large enough to be seen and given names or numbers. Most likely two or three rather small planets at one time moved in this orbit but came into collision and shattered. Analysis of meteorites that have arrived on Earth from this source shows that the heavy metallic or stony matter first solidified about 4,600 million years ago, according to their internal radioactive evidence, that is, at the time the solar system as a whole was taking shape and substance, and that the shattering occurred about 200 million years ago, relatively recently in cosmic or geological time, though long enough ago for human ancestors to have lived in lizard form. The largest of the asteroids is Ceres, 480 miles across. Because its shape is spherical and not irregular like all the rest, we conclude it has so far managed to avoid a collision. The others are smaller and all shapes and sizes of a most irregular kind, their exposed metal surfaces glinting in the Sun as they take their erratic course in the asteroidal zone. The culprit in this situation is Jupiter, whose Jovian force of gravity has played havoc with the orderly orbiting of small planets traveling nearby.

Jupiter is no quiescent giant, but turns on its axis in less than ten hours, blowing and rumbling as it spins around. A bright zone of clouds circles the equator, with a fierce westerly wind forever blowing in the equatorial region at two hundred miles an hour, similar to the jet stream in the atmosphere of the Earth. To the north and south are darker belts of clouds, with storm centers where the belts and the jet come together. Further south again is the south tropical belt, although there is no warmth in terrestrial terms. It is in this belt that the Great Red Spot, so-called, is frequently uncovered, large enough to be seen with small telescopes and with more than enough room to engulf three Earths. Astronomers at present think the Spot is some kind of solid object, 20,000 miles long and half that wide, floating in the Jovian atmosphere below the level of the clouds and drifting slowly westward. The suggestion is made that the island may be floating in an ocean of liquid hydrogen, beneath clouds of ammonia, though of what the island itself may consist, nothing has been said.

The atmosphere, however, has a temperature of $-200°$ F., cold enough to freeze out water and carbon dioxide and to condense the gases to liquid droplets.

Supposing in spite of all common sense a landing is attempted on Jupiter. As you entered the atmosphere you would dip through clouds of methane and ammonia crystals. As pressure and temperature increased somewhat, the ammonia crystals would liquefy and turn bronze and then blue. With further descent and increasing pressure all would become a murky sludge, until at last you landed on the solid surface of the planet. By this time you would be anything but weightless, and if you had weighed 170 pounds on Earth, you would now weigh about 365 on Jupiter, with your space capsule probably glued forevermore to the point of landing. Hard shells of ice undoubtedly cover the center of the planet, composed not only of water ice but of other kinds as well, including frozen hydrogen which would be present in great quantities. Extending about fifteen thousand miles from the center would be a heavy core containing iron and nickel and other of the heavier elements common on Earth. The equatorial bulge of Jupiter, like that of the Earth, shows such a core to be present. Altogether a most unpleasing prospect for colonists, though perhaps a good place to send our troublemakers, to the Hell of Dante's imagination.

Twelve moons circle around Jupiter, two of them as large as Mercury and two as big as the Moon, giants to fit their master. They are the four that were seen by Galileo as they circle the planet in a matter of hours in fascinating display. Those farther out and much smaller take 260 days to make the round; while the outermost two, which may be captured asteroids and not true moons at all, require two years.

Jupiter not only spins fast, accompanied by a ballet of

syncopated moons, but supplies its own radio orchestra. The planet transmits storm signals in the shortwave radio band, especially when storms pass close to the Red Spot, suggesting all manner of disturbances such as rain storms of liquid ammonia, icequakes at the surface, or true Jovian thunder. Certainly we are not quite so far gone ourselves that we think a Jovian form of intelligence exists and is trying to communicate with radio-plagued humanity.

Beyond Jupiter are the other giants—Saturn, Uranus, Neptune—not quite so large, and with surface gravity about the same as on Earth. The first two, at least, spin about as fast as Jupiter, and Neptune not much slower. But the cold increases—Saturn at −250° F., Uranus and Neptune at −300° F. Saturn's atmosphere resembles Jupiter's, but the atmospheres of the other two are mainly methane with only a trace of ammonia, although ammonia is probably present below to form more of the icy shells. Saturn's rings, wonderful to see, perplexed Galileo and the other early observers, for when the rings were edgewise to the Earth they could not be seen at all. When they are open, they are seen to be three, and nowhere to touch the planet. If they were solid the outer edge would be traveling faster than the inner, but it actually moves more slowly and must consist of a multitude of small ice particles moving in circular orbits around the planet, as though they were myriads of microscopic moons. Saturn's real moons are probably snowballs, and the rings may also once have been moons of ice, that were shattered by tides produced by the planet's mass. In any case Saturn and the remaining giants are apparently like Jupiter in having a central core of rock and iron surrounded by shells of ice of various kinds and an atmosphere of frozen gases. If at some distant time the Sun heats up and cooks the Earth and all that is upon it, the giants may one by one warm up and thaw, and then perhaps begin where the Earth began some billion years ago. Whether time enough would still remain for a repetition of the Earthly theme is something else again.

With so much ammonia around it seems inevitable that the question should be asked whether ammonia could be an alternative to water as a medium and basis for life. Certainly we must remember that life can exist in forms other than we can imagine. There, of course, is one of our difficulties. What cannot be imagined cannot be described, although it may be possible to set a course into the indescribable without being able to follow it to the point of visualization. In any case the question should be faced. We cannot assume that the only life in the universe is necessarily constructed mainly out of water and carbon, even though such may well turn out to be the case. There is no doubt that we breathe oxygen in consequence of the fact that we drink water. Jovian animals could breathe nitrogen and drink liquid ammonia. If not on Jupiter, maybe somewhere else in the great beyond.

However, let us put the cap on Jupiter and see how it fits. Life of any sort, if it is in any way to meet our conception, must contain and at first exist in a solvent, and must have a complex chemical and physical structure. To be a good solvent for the production and maintenance of life, a substance must meet several requirements. Above all it must be available; it must be a good insulation against heat and electricity; it must have a high specific heat in order to ensure some measure of thermal stability to the organism, that is, it shouldn't change too readily from liquid to a solid or a gas; and it must be able to flow and not be too sticky. Water meets these qualifications superbly, and others to boot, but ammonia also satisfies the basic requirements and cannot therefore be disqualified.

The structure of Earthly protoplasm is built around the

properties of carbon. So are the great variety of synthetic materials that make this the age of plastics. Carbon forms simple compounds with hydrogen, nitrogen, and oxygen. It also combines all the merits of this simplicity with the capacity to make rings and endless chains of carbon atoms, with all manner of side pieces. These form the architecture of cells, the rhythmically contractile proteins responsible for movement, the membranes that transmit messages, and structures that intercept the energy of light itself. If we substitute liquid ammonia for water, what happens to all this? Apparently not too much, for most of the characteristic structures could most likely be made with nitrogen taking a more prominent role and oxygen left out—that is, without the use of water.

If ever we succeed in reconstructing life in the laboratory using the Earthly components such as water, carbon dioxide, and oxygen, then we may try our hands with ammonia in place of water. An ammonia-based life is at least conceivable. Yet, if we are right in thinking that the inner, or terrestrial, planets originally possessed an ammonia-methane atmosphere, and the outer planets still have such an atmosphere, why hasn't the opportunity been taken here in this solar system—or has it? One answer is that liquid ammonia, the only kind we are concerned with, seems to be too fussy about its temperature. In liquid state it exists only within a range less than half that of water, between its boiling point at $-28°$ F. and its melting point at -98 °F. In our solar system a planet would find an orbit fitting to such a state somewhere between that of Mars and Jupiter and nowhere else. Jupiter itself is too far out, Mars too far in. If any planet could have demonstrated the possibility, only one that took the orbit of asteroids could have done so. If it had any ideas along this line, a jealous nearby Jupiter has knocked them to smithereens.

So much for the solar system. What lies beyond? Are there other solar systems as good as this, with one or more planets supporting life?

Out beyond the solar system, quite a way out, lie the other stars of our particular galaxy. And beyond this, scattered through the visible universe and farther yet, are billions upon billions of other galaxies, each with myriad stars of its own. The void is great and the cosmic wind blows chill into the soul if not the body. Company would be welcome.

Knowing already a little too much about our immediate neighbors, the planets we can see, our minds reach out to possible planets beyond our ken, where imagination can people them with such as used to be on the Moon and Mars. It will be sad if the time ever comes when the mind cannot go where the body cannot follow, leaving us trapped by our mortality and other Earthly nuisances. Yet even for dreams there must be something to build on. A slight wobble of a distant star is enough to get us started, and the Milky Way is far enough to go.

There are stars aplenty to choose among, though for the present at least we should look at the lot. Astronomers tell us they are suns of sorts, of which our own sun is a pretty average representative. Two kinds predominate—hot, blue stars with a short starlife, as starlives go, and not-so-hot but yellower stars made of a richer star dust, as long-lived as the one that warms us. Speaking in cosmic time, blue stars are here today and gone tomorrow, with no time at all to evoke a living thing even if all else were right. Of the others, do they have planets or not? That is the question. Can we go on dreaming, or do we wake up not only to a cold isolation but to solitary confinement for eternity, or at least for as long as this Earth shall last? What ever else is involved, our peace of mind appears to be at stake.

A generation ago a planetary system such as ours was thought to be the result of two stars coming into near-collision, swinging round one another in a flurry, and drawing out a stream of stellar matter by gravitational force—great tides that spewed out globs to become orbiting satellites when all was quiet again. Whatever explanatory merit this theory may have had, it was discouraging in other ways, for it said in effect that only in the extremely rare event of two stars approaching one another in just this way was there a chance that a solar system would form. This would have left us not necessarily unique in the universe, but certainly so unusual and rare as to be merely one of several freaks instead of the only one. The reinstatement of man in the scheme of things received no support.

The contemporary view that a solar system is a natural consequence of the condensation of stellar dust to form a star, under certain conditions of size and rotation, has changed our outlook profoundly. No chance encounter with another star is required, and what has happened here may have been and may still be an everyday occurrence, so to speak, especially since our sun and even our galaxy seem to follow the rule of mediocrity—neither better nor worse nor significantly different from the majority. Even if all cosmological theories, whether of solar systems, galaxies, or the universe as a whole, are, as one noted astronomer has called them, merely bubbles of pure thought, we are simply being human in producing them. We, as a solar system, as a planet bearing life, or as a particular kind of intelligent life blessed or cursed with self-awareness, do not wish to stick out like a sore little thumb on the enormous body of the cosmos. We feel we belong, as individuals, together with all that is about us, in spite of the immensities of space and time and numbers of the star-studded heavens.

All stars cannot have planets and all planetary systems cannot be suitable for life, however heartwarming the contrary might be. To be suitable for the emergence and evolution of life to the point that has been reached on Earth, a star with its planets must persist in stable form for at least several billion years. Not all stars do so. Those more or less similar to the Sun in mass, with the same yellow color and surface chemistry, appear to take a fairly well defined course from birth to death. A star a little larger than the Sun, for instance, condenses from a dust cloud into a star and protoplanets in something like ten million years, a relatively fleeting episode in cosmic time. It then enters the state known as the main sequence, in which it remains for some eight billion years. At the end of this time it expands into the red-giant stage, a period of about one hundred million years, during which time it burns up any attendant planets one by one. Finally, after flickering for some thousands of years, it explodes into a nova, sending out star matter into space and collapsing at the heart into a white dwarf.

When stars such as this enter the main sequence, a curious change is usually observed. Their rapid rotation abruptly slows down. The explanation now generally accepted is that unobservable planets have absorbed the so-called angular momentum, just as Jupiter and the other planets of our solar system now carry 98 per cent of the angular momentum, or momentum of revolution, leaving the Sun with only 2 per cent and a long 27-day period of rotation. If planets do account for the slow spin of the sun-like stars then planets exist in conjunction with the stars most likely to support life.

In our own galaxy, the only one where stars have been studied individually, somewhat more than ten per cent fall into this category. Even so, with roughly 200 billion stars altogether in the galaxy, more than 20 billion may accordingly have planets and may have had them long enough for planets to have produced advanced and possibly intelligent forms of life. Remember, too, that the Milky Way is but one among billions of galaxies that constitute the visible universe. And nowhere in the universe is there any indication that one part of the universe is different from another in the nature of its matter. Wherever a star shines upon its planets, and planets keep within bounds, the few commonest and lightest elements at their surface will join each other in a dance of life. The stage is there and the curtain raised. Who are the actors?

Out of Their Minds

Observe how system into system runs,
What other planets circle other suns,
What varied beings people every star.

So wrote Alexander Pope some while ago.

There are planets galore, all sizes if not all shapes, some in the right place, most in the wrong place, some of the right stuff and some that are not. How do we people them, those that are wellborn and well bred?

Peopling unseen planets, with various degrees of plausibility and predilection, has been a popular pastime for a good many years. Science fiction depends upon it. Most of it is imagination runaway, though Jules Verne, in his first long shot at it, took a very cautious stand which can be our point of departure. In the words of his spokesman:

"If I were a natural philosopher, I would tell him that if less energy were set in motion upon the planets which are nearest the sun, and more upon those which are farthest removed from it, this simple fact would alone

suffice to equalize the heat, and to render the temperature of those worlds supportable by beings organized
like ourselves. If I were a naturalist, I would tell him
that according to some illustrious men of Science, Nature
has furnished us with instances upon the earth of animals existing under very varying conditions of life; that
fish respire in a medium fatal to other animals; that
amphibious creatures possess a double existence very
difficult of explanation; that certain denizens of the Seas
maintain life at enormous depths, and there support a
pressure equal to that of fifty or sixty atmospheres without being crushed; that several aquatic insects, insensible
to temperature, are met with equally among boiling
springs and in the frozen plains of the Polar Sea; in fine,
that we cannot help recognizing in nature a diversity of
means of operation often times incomprehensible, but
not the less real. If I were a chemist, I would tell him
that the meteorites—bodies evidently formed exteriorly
of our terrestrial globe—have, upon analysis, revealed
indisputable traces of carbon, a substance which owes its
origin solely to organized beings, and which must necessarily have been imbued with animation itself. And
lastly, were I a theologian, I would tell him that the
scheme of the Divine Redemption, according to Paul,
seems to be applicable, not merely to the earth, but to
all celestial worlds. But, unfortunately I am neither
theologian, nor chemist, nor naturalist, nor philosopher;
therefore in my absolute ignorance of the great laws
which govern the universe, I confine myself to saying
that I do not know whether the worlds are inhabited or
not; and since I do not know, *I am going to see!*"

The writer's imagination appears to have failed when
his voyagers take off, for apart from postulating lunar sub-

surface serpentine shapes he leaves the matter well enough alone. Not so his successors, H. G. Wells and Edgar Rice Burroughs, not to mention the crowd which came later, although Wells, after a first careless rapture on the Moon, was wiser when he came to Mars. Nowadays peopling the Moon and Mars is too implausible, and science fictioneers have to go to the great unknown to find sufficient freedom. So in due courtesy we should transport the creatures of Wells' and Burroughs' imagination to the planets of other solar systems where they might feel more at home.

Wells was an academically qualified student of biology and his first book was a textbook of zoology. This experience undoubtedly supplied material for his fertile mind to work on and at the same time put at least some reins upon it. Even so his man in the moon is something to marvel at:

> "the slender, pinched body and short and extremely attenuated bandy legs of a Selenite, with his head depressed between his shoulders . . . walked like a bird . . . it wasn't a face . . . there were no ears . . . there was a mouth, downwardly curved, like a human mouth in a face that stares ferociously . . . the neck on which the head was poised was jointed in three places, almost like the short joints in the leg of a crab . . . the joints of the limbs I could not see!"

The parts are recognizable but the whole is not, for this is a creature that reflects bits and pieces of the animal kingdom, like some mythical combination beast of medieval times. Yet the man is there, with his two staring eyes and bipedal gait, and breathing air if he breathed at all. Whether of the Moon or elsewhere this being doesn't ring true, and Wells must have known it, for in *The War of the Worlds,* where he has Martians landing on Earth, he dodges the question. His Martians arrive in impenetrable capsules which maneuver by means of rods and levers, much as men are now planning to do when they actually do land on a nearby planet, but the Martian himself is never seen and therefore requires no description. He is only the hidden intelligence, sensitive and aware, operating the apparatus from within.

Another generation later, weaned on Wells as Wells was on Verne, Edgar Rice Burroughs, whose Tarzan later spawned the comic strip space supermen, in turn staged his dramatic fantasies on the planets. For the most part his planets and their moons are populated with beings like ordinary humans except for their red or green color, or in having two pairs of arms. With them are a motley assortment of wild and weird creatures, including horses with eight legs and lions and dogs each with ten legs. The more outstanding characters deserve full descriptions and these are taken from an appendix to one of the Martian romances:

"The Apt: An Arctic monster. A huge, white-furred creature with six limbs, four of which, short and heavy, carry it over the snow and ice; the other two, which grow forward from its shoulders on either side of its long, powerful neck, terminate in white, hairless hands with which it seizes and holds its prey. Its head and mouth are similar in appearance to those of a hippopotamus except that from the sides of the lower jawbone two mighty horns curve slightly downward toward the front. Its two huge eyes extend in two vast oval patches from the center of the top of the cranium down either side of the head to below the roots of the horns, so that these weapons really grow from the lower part of the eyes, which are composed of several thousand ocelli each. Each ocellus is furnished with its own lid, and the apt can, at will, close as many of the facets of his huge eyes as he chooses."

"The Sith: Hornet-like monster. Bald-faced and about the size of a Hereford bull. Has frightful jaws in front and mighty poisoned sting behind. The eyes, of myriad facets, cover three-fourths of the head, permitting the creature to see in all directions at one and the same time."

And, finally, here we go!—the "Plant Men of Barsoom: They are ten or twelve feet in height when standing erect; their arms are very short and fashioned after the manner of an elephant's trunk, being sinuous; the body is hairless and ghoulish blue except for a broad band of white which encircles the protruding, single eye, the pupil, iris, and ball of which are dead white. The nose is a ragged, inflamed, circular hole in the center of the blank face, resembling a fresh bullet wound which has not yet commenced to bleed. There is no mouth in the head. With the exception of the face, the head is covered by a tangled mass of jet-black hair some eight or ten inches in length. Each hair is about the thickness of a large angleworm. The body, legs and feet are of human shape but of monstrous proportions, the feet being fully three feet long and very flat and broad. The method of feeding consists in running their odd hands over the turf, cropping off the tender vegetation with razor-like talons and sucking it up from two mouths, which lie one in the palm of each hand. They are equipped with a massive tail about six feet long, quite round where it joins the body, but tapering to a flat, thin blade toward the end, which trails at right angles to the ground."

A few items in the narrative are left out of this catalog of plant-men characteristics, for elsewhere they are said to be green and to contain green juice in place of red blood, and to have a second pair of arms, midway between shoulders and hips. And to cap it all—"By far the most remarkable feature of this most remarkable creature, however, were the two tiny replicas of it, each about six inches in length, which dangled, one on each side, from its armpits. They were suspended by a small stem which seemed to grow from the exact tops of their heads to where it connected them with the body of the adult. . . . The little ones varied in size from what appeared to be but tiny unopened buds an inch in diameter through various stages of development to the full-fledged and perfectly formed creature of ten to twelve inches in length. Feeding with the herd were many of the little fellows not much larger than those attached to their parents, and from the young of that size the herd graded up to the immense adults." Although plant-croppers, they also had a taste for blood, sucking in the manner of a lamprey, and in keeping with this would attack other creatures ferociously, bounding over the heads of their prey and slashing lethally with their heavy tails.

Never in the history of biologically flavored fiction has there been such a mix-up. Practically all of it is taken from living realities, but as a complete scramble of pieces from the plant and animal kingdoms, with something of human bipedalism thrown in to weight the horror. The subsequent generation of science fiction writers has not approached this peak or even tried to do so. For the most part the later speculations have stayed as closely within the bounds of plausibility as possible. And this of course is about all we can attempt to do if we are to feel out the possibilities of life forms on planets we may never reach or see. Nevertheless, Burroughs' plant-men merit a brief examination to see what the mixture really is.

So far as the obviously human types first mentioned are concerned, they may as well be red or green as the various

degrees of yellow-brown colors typical of ourselves. Adding
an extra pair of arms is clearly inspired by the paintings
and sculptures of Hindu religion. Such a condition might
have arisen in the course of human evolution, but it did
not, and there are some rather effective rules against it.
The same applies to the multilegged lions, dogs, and horses
—unnecessary multiplicity of parts is detrimental to efficiency and is unlikely to be tolerated in a large animal, as
we shall see.

The Apts and the Siths, for what they are worth, are
obviously backboned creatures and the former even quali-
fies as a furry mammal, but the eyes are patterned after the
insect's, superficially at least; certainly eyes that see virtually in all directions are not unknown among insects and
spiders. The mixture is simple enough and a four-legged,
two-armed creature with compound arthropodan eyes
could conceivably exist, but not as a vertebrate animal
since it implies a mix-up at the material construction level,
like building with adobe and with glass and steel at the
same time.

The plant-men are more interesting. Bipeds as tall as
they, with a great tail, were the tyrants of the Earth during
the Age of Reptiles, and some of their relatives had heavy
spikes of a lethally offensive nature at the end of the tail.
The large flat feet appear to be the human type magnified.
Four sinuous sucking arms, elephant's trunks misplaced
and multiplied, obviously with no internal supporting or
interfering skeleton, are an obvious but senseless shift of
a subdivided nose. The single eye, of a camera type, in the
middle of the head—a Cyclops in fact—is familiar in the
story of the Odyssey and also as a monstrous human condition that does not usually survive birth; its lack of pigment
in iris and pupil is incompatible with function, as though
a camera were transparent. The angleworm hair suggests

he Gorgon but makes no sense. Green body juice could be
blood—certainly not sap, for even green plants do not have
green sap; blood does not need to be red—many creatures
have pale blue blood and there is a group of worms which
has green. As for reproduction, why shouldn't new individuals grow as buds from the old? It happens not only in
plants but in many of the lower forms of animal life; there
is nothing startling in the idea itself, but only in the combination of such a process with the size and way of life of
one-eyed dinosaur that jumps like a kangaroo.

Taking all this together we find nothing new, but only
strangeness deliberately obtained by putting familiar
things together in incompatible ways and exaggerating or
multiplying or misplacing otherwise ordinary features.
These imaginative exercises, if we can call them that,
served their purpose in the stories, but they obviously
throw more light on the human way of thought than on real
life anywhere in the universe. At the same time they call
attention to the difficulty and perhaps the impossibility of
imagining something completely strange. Certainly the
usual cartoon of spacemen encountering the unearthly
but intelligent inhabitants of other planets illustrates this,
for inevitably these supposedly strange creatures are all too
human—typical bipeds on land, differing from ourselves
mainly in size, shape of nose and ears, and too often the
presence of a pair of forehead tentacles.

We can only work with what we know, to begin with at
least, but there are rules of procedure which must be recognized if progress is to be made. The zoologist has already
had some experience along such lines, for the whole business of determining how present forms of animal life have
evolved from relatively simple and often very different
primitive forms of the distant past has much in common

with the process of projecting life forms onto other planet
where circumstances also are different.

One of the basic principles, for instance, in working ou
the nature of Earthly life forms which are now extinct, bu
must have at one time existed in order to account for th
presence and special nature of various living organism
now present, is that *at all times* our reconstruction of pas
types must represent organisms capable of complete, ha
monious functioning under the prevailing circumstance
All fossil remains have of course been invaluable. Fossi
found are first examined to see whether any are whol
creatures and, second, how the part determines the specia
nature of the whole. Admittedly we are dealing with mor
or less familiar kinds of animals, for the living world rep
resents the past, transformed to a greater or lesser degree
The process is akin to reconstructing the nature of som
old-fashioned kind of clock on the basis of having foun
a part recognized to be that of a clock, and from what w
know of how clocks work. In both cases insight is require
in order to reconstruct the whole so that the part fits ha
moniously and the whole works efficiently.

Any speculation concerning the nature of life on distan
planets necessarily depends on our understanding of life o
Earth, since as yet we know no other. This understandin
concerns three aspects of life—an understanding of eac
kind of living thing as a successfully functioning organis
at the present time, an understanding of the whole inte
woven web of life of the Earth, in all its interdependenc
and in its relation to the Sun, and an understanding of ho
it has all come to be, as a whole, in relation to the plane
and as individual component parts. So far as we can tell, th
Earth has had a solid crust for more than four billion year
The oldest fossilized traces of life are in rocks at least tw
billion years old, and these traces represent organized, ind

pendent, plantlike cells—already a tremendous achievement in the evolution of life.

To be on the safe side we have to allot a minimum of three billion years to the process of evolution of Earthly life from its inception to its present glory. During this period both life and the planet itself have undergone remarkable changes. And at all stages life as a whole and as particular kinds of life has evolved in response to the nature of its surroundings, which includes both cosmic and planetary influences and also the nature of the world of life itself. So much therefore depends on what has been inevitable as the result of Earthly circumstances of a general sort, such as the particular nature of the planet situated as it is at a certain distance from a particular type of star, and what have been virtually fortuitous developments that the slightest change might have prevented or diverted. To put it in a nutshell, if conditions on Earth had at any time been different, would the living community as a whole have been much different and, in particular, could human beings have come into existence? We do know that mankind has emerged in recognizable form only during the last two million years, during the last second of geological time. Has man been inevitable from the beginning, so very long ago? And what are the chances that anything comparable to ourselves, or to any of the diverse living things known to us here, may exist elsewhere in the universe?

When speculative ice is as thin as this we need to approach it gingerly, from the safe ground of the known onto the edge of the unknown, rather than make the long jump toward the middle of the pond. At least it is a way to begin and possibly to make some progress before we become engulfed. It is a game that anyone can play, and there is no end to it. The aim is to work out how different the animals or plants might be if some change had been made in the

circumstances to which they have become adapted; how
different a particular biological situation might be if some
contributing factor had been otherwise, whether of the en
vironment or of a biological process or mechanism. Time
enters into the picture. Small changes introduced toward
the end of a long developing process, whether of evolution
or of the development of a human or other individual, may
have comparatively minor effects, whereas similar changes
during early stages could lead to an outcome either dis
astrous or profoundly different. Or the game can be started
from the other side by changing the planet in various ways
—in size, density, spin, axis inclination, location in a solar
system, and past duration. The only limit is our ingenuity
—and the need to keep in mind that we ourselves are the
matter of one planet come alive, that is now trying to en
visage the matter of some other planet which has also come
alive.

Gravity Gets You Down

THE EARTH has a certain mass and that mass holds every-thing to it as though by a magnet. If we leap from a height we are pulled by mother Earth into one last and squashy embrace. The force of gravity is the most fundamental in the universe and the least understood, and all suns and planets are predicated on it. And all forms of life denser than their surroundings have to cope with it. Such is the fate of man from the cradle to the grave.

This the force that holds matter to itself—the heaviest to the heaviest and the lightest to the lightest, so that the Earth has a heavy heart, a lighter but stony mantle, an outer film of liquid water through which stone will sink, and an outermost envelope of gases, the lightest stuff of all. The whole is as though the original mixture of Earth had been spun in a giant centrifuge to separate the constituents according to their density, with the lightest of all tending to fly off into the vacuum of space—as most of the Earth's hydrogen almost certainly has done. What now lies below the crust is known mainly from the behavior of earthquake waves and the molten rock which occasionally spews forth through volcanoes, although any conclusions we can draw from the study of metallic and stony meteorites landing here from somewhere else, the actual fragments of a shattered planet, are certainly relevant. In any case, life in all its kinds and shapes contends with and in intricate ways is a part of the thin outer planetary veils of gas and water external to the solid crust.

Although comparisons at times are odious, they are generally illuminating. This would be evident to the first men on the Moon if only they could be free and unencapsulated. Wells gives a vivid account of what such an experience might be, if wandering on the Moon were unimpeded:

> "Then I made a hasty step to look over the verge of a rock. . . . The thrust of my foot that I made in striding would have carried me a yard on earth; on the moon it carried me six—a good five yards over the edge. For the moment the thing had something of the effect of those nightmares when one falls and falls. For while one falls sixteen feet in the first second of a fall on earth, on the moon one falls two, and with only a sixth of one's weight. I fell, or rather I jumped down, about ten yards I suppose. It seemed to take quite a long time, five or six seconds, I should think. I floated through the air and fell like a feather, knee-deep in a snow-drift in the bottom of a gulley of blue-gray, white-veined rock. . . . I had forgotten that on the moon, with only an eighth part of the earth's mass and a quarter of its diameter, my weight was barely one sixth what it was on earth. But now the fact insisted on being remembered."

In contrast to the Moon, though staying within this solar system, is Jupiter, with a force of gravity of about two and one-half times as great at its surface as on the Earth. On such a planet, placed in an orbit where men could live, the same forward thrust of the foot would carry it no more than fifteen inches, for the swinging leg is much like a pendulum whose swing is limited by the braking pull of gravity. Moreover, falling from the height of a stool under the same circumstance would have as damaging an impact as a fall from the top of a ladder would on Earth.

To see how different various kinds of living things might be if the planet Earth was actually the size of Jupiter, if the force of gravity were more than double what it is, some appreciation of how gravity already affects the living world is desirable. For in all our speculations the Earth and its living freight has to be the yardstick.

The effect of gravity depends on where one lives— whether in the air, on land, or in the water. The Earth, so to speak, clearly has a place for everything and everything in its place, although all is relative. What is heavier sinks through what is lighter, and that which is lighter rises through the heavier, as long as the medium permits such movement. Fish and jellyfish may be of the same density as the water around them, and to all intent gravity might be non-existent. Scallops, crabs, and lobsters have relatively heavy shells and are pulled inexorably through the water to the solid floor of the sea. On land all living things are beings out of water, have the solid earth beneath them, but otherwise are engulfed in air. The force of gravity is fully felt and generally difficult to deal with. And in the air itself all animate bodies are dense and are kept aloft only by acrobatic motion.

Look around at this Earth, particularly where life is most in evidence. Trees abound, where human whim permits, and grow to various heights, the greatest rising to two or three hundred feet. Four-footed animals roam among them, ranging in size from small mice and shrews to the giraffes, hippopotami, and elephants. All have their problems. So far as gravity is concerned, all have to support their own weight, all have to cope with the compression of weight upon their own tissues and structure, most have to propel fluid against the downward pull of gravity, and, in addition, the animals have to lever their bodies over the ground. And all are organic things that have come out of the water at some distant time in the past—paradoxically both wet and combustible—yet are now elevating themselves, and are either reaching for the Sun or living a perambulating existence.

Take the seemingly simple question of a tree. Like any plant out of water it has a crown of leaves exposed to the light, where the business of making the new stuff of life goes on; and at the base it has a ramifying system of roots probing in search of water to pass to the leaves. This much is true of any plant that lives on land. What makes a tree a tree is the vertical distance from roots to leaves—how tall the column of conducting tubes that run from the roots to the transpiring top—and how great a canopy has to be supplied. By subtle combinations of pull and push the living tissues raise fine columns of water to surprising heights against the downward drag of the Earth itself. It is a feat any way you look at it, like a pyramid of acrobats. But like such a pyramid, what reaches the top must be supported in addition to being put there.

The trunk of a tree has a relatively broad base and tapers upward and generally keeps its top directly above its base. The fight against gravity is now engaged in earnest. A felled tree crashes with an earth-shaking impact and its weight is tremendous. That weight, at its greatest, is supported by the bole of the tree, by the organic, life-manufactured combinations of hydrogen, carbon, and oxygen which we call wood. The wonder is that so delicate a substance can cope with so much. Yet if a tree fails to keep its head above its feet, over it goes. And if any particular kind of tree grows too high for the tensile strength of its woody column, it will bend and break, just as will a steel mast that is too high for its width.

Raising water, resisting the crushing effect of weight, and maintaining an effective balance are all contentions against the pull of gravity. Altogether they determine how much of a tree a tree shall be. Change the force of gravity and you change the tree. Lessen it and trees could be slimmer though not necessarily taller. Increase it and they will be stouter and shorter, in general stumpy, sturdier types than are common on Earth. And so with a man. So much weight is supported by so much bone and the weight of the whole is borne by the products of living tissue. Change the force of gravity, though leaving living substance as it is, and you change the shape or size of man, if not his nature.

Gravity gets us down. If you trip over something you fall with a thud that breaks your nose or cracks your skull. Keeping head and trunk over feet is as necessary to a standing man as it is to a tree. Trees have been made for it, however, whereas man has not; and from the time we begin to crawl till the time we can no longer get out of bed, gravity takes its toll in one way or another. Cast a quick look back over your own progress and see how it goes.

To begin with you were on all fours and all the safer for it, with the weight of the body slung between four corner posts and everything inside resting as if in a hammock. Then came the tremendous though long-forgotten struggle by which you learned to stand upright, balancing on your two hind limbs, ready to fall if you swayed a little or stepped too slow or fast in an effort to walk. As the body grew heavier the load increased, ankles turned in, knees turned in or out, bones bent a little, and the straight-legged beauty that might have been has a warped and rickety look. Eventually you stood fully grown, so far as height is concerned, though all too ready to sit or lie down whenever the chance arose. Then the peak is past. Weight increases in a roundabout way and the load increases again, but with waning strength to support it. Arches begin to fall, pouches form beneath the eyes, and stomachs begin to sag as the strength of muscle and fiber weaken and the tug of gravity draws us closer to the Earth. Compression also takes its toll and the weight of the brain-filled head and heavier trunk wearing day by day, year after year, upon the spongy disks between the vertebrae wears them thin and they start to slip. Finally the body bends over, and too often only the support of a heavy cane prevents a return to the quadrupedal state. Such is the rise and fall of man during his span of life as a slave to a force he does not yet understand.

If the Earth were as big as Jupiter and bodies the size of ours weighed two and a half times as much, nothing could be the same. Anyone like the average man would suffer the disadvantages of extreme obesity, though not the bulk. The human baby at birth or thereabouts would weigh between twenty and thirty pounds, and more than fifty when the time came to stand upright in the world. The puny legs would never take the strain and the human being would remain on all fours for all its life—with relief in every joint, and hands less free for mischief. Perhaps it would be better so, though certainly depressing in a general way.

For man to be man under such conditions, something would have to be different. A fullgrown man would deteriorate under his own weight much faster than he normally does—feet would break down, disks would slip, insides would sag and middles bulge, and any fall would crack a bone or tear ligaments asunder. And levering the whole thing along by pulling with muscles and tendons would be so effortful and burdensome that few would ever get started. It is tiresome enough as it is.

Obviously, then, if the Earth were so overpowering, man could not retain, or have evolved, his present shape or size. One or the other perhaps, but not both. It is a matter for a construction engineer. One approach is to see what full-grown men would be like if their body weight was no more than one hundred and fifty pounds in a Jovian force of gravity—which would be the same as sixty pounds on Earth. What would a sixty-pound man be like if he were carrying an effective load two to three times as great? Much as if he were a boy of eight with the bodily burden of a man. Some thickening of leg bones and a general strengthening of ligaments would be necessary, but probably not much else.

The greater difference would appear if man were to be his present size, for then his grown weight here would be close to a fifth of a ton and a change in proportions would be called for. As in the tree, all that lies above has to be supported by a cross-section of the base, in this case of the leg bones, particularly at the lower end. To be as strong as they are they would need to be nearly twice as thick, not like an elephant's, to be sure, but certainly like a cow's. To move such a body with the ease we are accustomed to, such as it is, leg and thigh muscles would have to match the thickened skeleton, especially those striding muscles that so seductively shape our ends. With big, flat feet, massive legs, and larger behinds we would be bumptious bipeds indeed. Whether man under such grave circumstances would have needed to evolve to his present stature would depend mainly on what competition he had to meet.

The force of gravity determines so much of what is taken for granted in the world, particularly of the size and shape and locomotion of the animals about us. It is a common mistake to think that large creatures run faster than small, yet a dog can keep up with a horse and, with very few exceptions, the upper speed limit for all is about thirty-five miles an hour. It is safer to be big if you are of the kind that others like to eat, for large size itself can be used in a defensive-offensive manner, but it is not wise to sacrifice speed to bulk unless bulk is carried to the extreme. So what we see when we look at a horse is what a horse has to be if it is to be as big as it is and run as well as a dog. And it is gravity that calls the tune.

The fossil record of horses is better known than is that of any comparable mammal; the gradual transformation of dog-sized, three-toed creatures to one-toed, long-legged, long-faced, long-necked, half-ton beasts in the shape of a horse during the past fifty to sixty million years can be followed step by step. The main point of interest is that here is an animal becoming steadily larger through untold generations, though it is better to say a group of animals, because a group of horses evolved and not merely the one genus that still survives, until weight alone put a stop to the process. The force of gravity determines what weight the self-propelling living machinery can carry. If gravity were more or less, so would be the horse, though in an inverse way. As it is, anything bigger than the horse could not be as good a horse—the heaviest horses in fact, the dray horses, have the weight and muscle power to pull enough ale for a year of Sundays, but they are too heavy and slow ever to have run with the wild.

So, steadily, as the years rolled on by the million, horsy things grew bigger, always ready to run and to run like the wind. The higher their shoulders, the longer the neck stretched to reach the ground to crop the grass, and the longer the snout so that eyes could still watch for approaching danger. As the body grew heavier and the legs became longer, leg bones fused into single structures of great strength like hollow steel rods, and feet became single-toed, long, well-shod, driving pistons for pushing hard and fast against the ground in the effort to propel forward the ever-heavier body. The limit was called in two ways. The upper limit to speed could not be passed because harder and faster driving at the ground only wore out faster the hoofs and operating machinery without adding speed. And no further change in the leg skeleton and in the bulk of the great operating muscles could be made to compensate for further increase in body weight. The living substance that spells horse on any other creature can stand just so much of the punishment inflicted by the pull of the Earth on things moving over the surface of the land.

On a smaller planet with weaker gravity a horse might be larger and leggier, but where gravity is much greater the requirements that led to the typical shape and special structure of the horse would operate at a lower level—horses could be but of the size of sheep. Otherwise, with several times their weight, they might in a sense exist, but only as clumsy, lumbering creatures no longer able to flee from danger.

We see such a creature in the elephant. This represents about as heavy a load of flesh and bone as can be moved around under its own power on the Earth's solid surface. Elephants, weighing several tons, not only support their body when standing still but swing it along alternatingly on one diagonal pair of legs or the other, when each leg underpins a load of close to two tons. Consequently the legs have to be massive though flexible pillars, for otherwise they would buckle under the load. Moreover feet can no longer do much levering of the leg and body off the ground, in the manner in which we employ our own feet. The elephant foot is mainly a thick pad below the ankle, and the elephant legs are swung from the shoulders and hips somewhat like tree trunks being continually placed in new upright positions as the overhead load is moved along. Bigger loads and correspondingly thicker legs would make the creature practically immovable, and even as it is an elephant depends mostly on its bulk and hardly at all on speed for safety.

Some of the dinosaurs of the Age of Reptiles were larger, to be sure, but they apparently spent most of their time partly submerged in swamps and rivers, browsing on aquatic vegetation, with a considerable part of the body weight supported by the water. And the largest of all creatures that have ever lived, the giant whales that weigh a hundred tons out of water, can attain such bulk only because it is entirely water-borne, just as a person is when swimming or floating. There are limits of course even to the size of a whale, but they are not related to gravity.

On a planet with an increased force of gravity whales and such would therefore be unaffected, but elephants, already at the limit in shape and construction for carrying heavy loads on land, could only exist on a smaller scale. This is not the same as merely dwarfing the elephant but making it smaller without lessening the load it carries here. Somehow it doesn't seem to work. The legs that would be necessary to support and move the smaller but just as heavy body would need to be as thick as they are and would therefore be too much out of proportion for the living machinery as a whole. To keep the legs within bounds the load would have to be lightened, so that nothing really remains the same.

With this sort of thing in mind let us continue our role of armchair creators and see if we can evolve a man on a planet as large as Jupiter but as close to the Sun as the Earth. Man, as we have seen, is not only essentially a fish

out of water endeavoring to stay wet inside while dry outside, but has had an arboreal phase of evolution which
transformed him from a small, four-footed, smell-obsessed,
litter-bearing mammal into a biped with hands, stereoscopic vision, an eye-hand brain with almost no sense of
smell, and the production of offspring usually one at a
time. We are grounded again now but without that ascent
and descent man could not be man. So here is the question.
Could all this have happened in much the same way to
produce what we would recognize or admit as human
under the conditions proposed? For trees would be shorter
and stouter, and climbing creatures would feel the pull of
gravity to a much greater degree.

The answer is, most likely, yes, if trees still grew close together to make a forest and consequently formed an overhead world which offered safety, light, room, and good
pickings, and demanded space vision, hands, and trapeze
work. This much makes an ape but leaves him sitting in a
tree. To become a man he has to come down and run on
his two hind, handlike feet. Since we are none too sure how
this came about in our own late evolution, whether trees
grew too far apart or apes just too heavy, or both, it is
harder to see what could happen if gravity were not what
it is. But the chances are that if any kind of forests produced any kind of ape-like beings, some of them, sooner or
later, would get too big for their place or venture into
sparser regions and have to come down to earth, for one of
the characteristics of evolving nature is that she so often
seems not to know where to stop. Shorter and heavier they
might be, but we could call them human if we stretched a
point. At least it is somewhat comforting to think that the
force of gravity could be very much greater without dis-
carding altogether the chance of something becoming human, always assuming that some form of animated life had

taken the right evolutionary path leading to the base of the tree.

So much for the monkey folk, up and down, and their four-footed friends about them. What about the birds and the bees, not to mention the flowers, on our imaginary overweighted planet? Insects and birds are both airborne and apart from intermittent rest must continuously fight or exploit the force of gravity or else tumble to the ground. And each has his own range of size and wing-operating mechanism. Birds range from the albatross down to the hummingbird and insects range from the hummingbird moth to a barely visible midge. In range of size there is virtually no overlapping between bird and insect. And wings beat according to size, from the great gliding but rarely flapping wings of the albatross to the hummingbird's that beat so fast that only a blur is to be seen, and from the similar beat of the hummingbird moth, or of the bee, to that of a midge that may beat more than a thousand times a second. It is all a matter of weight, wing beat and muscle, and the density and pressure of air. The first and last are related to gravity. The other is not.

Birds and insects are flying machines. What makes them what they are? To begin with, all excess luggage has been thrown overboard, at least in the case of birds. Insects had none to start with. Birds have hollowed out their bones to the limit compatible with strength—the man-o'-war bird, for instance, the fastest flyer on Earth, with a seven-foot wing spread, has little more than four ounces of bone altogether. Air sacs extend throughout the body, further lightening it and serving also as air reservoirs for the lungs to supply the great wing muscles of the keel. It adds up to lightness, strength and power, together with a streamlined shape that reduces air resistance to a minimum. Small birds must beat their wings rapidly to keep aloft. Large birds may have more difficulty getting up, but are more adept at exploiting air currents once they get there. The upper limit to the size of birds is not their total weight, for that problem has been overcome. It is the mass and bulk of the breast muscles necessary to operate the wings against air substance and their own inertia. The breast keel to which these muscles are attached cannot be longer than the body of the bird, nor can the keel and its muscles stick out too far or the machinery becomes inoperable. If a man could fly, with birdlike arms or with angel wings grown from his shoulder blades, he would require a breast keel and associated muscles a yard deep to develop power enough.

Insects have no such troubles, though they do have their own. They are small enough and light enough in any case and their wings are operated by powerful muscles in a tricky and indirect way that does not concern us here. Their small size—for even the largest is small compared to any bird or four-footed creature—is a restriction imposed by their mechanism for respiration. Oxygen is not carried to the muscles by circulating blood, as in the other creatures, but directly to the body tissues by means of branching air tubes. This system works exceedingly well if the length of the life lines is not too great and if the branches supplying the oxygen-hungry muscles do not get too fine and crowded. Double the length of an insect, however, and the air tube total must be cubed. So insect bodies are small to remain efficient. How efficient, you can tell by listening to the buzz of a bee or a fly as it whizzes by your ear. And just as everything about a bird is adjusted to the density of air as a medium to press against in order to move, so the air tube muscle supply system of an insect is adjusted to the atmospheric pressure which pushes air into the life-giving tubes.

Birds and insects seem to be closely associated, though

not in pedigree. It may well be, in fact, that the flightless
insect forerunners left the water primarily to escape being
eaten, that aquatic vertebrates left the water to continue
eating them, that insects took to the air to escape again,
and that birds, and eventually the mammalian bats, became airborne to follow them—each time with a lag of the
order of one hundred million years between escape and
follow-up. They are all part of the same act, performed on
the same stage. What happens to the act if gravity is increased by two or three times?

This is a subtler question, because more is involved than
the creatures alone. The air itself, at the inhabited levels,
would be denser to the same degree—increasing the air resistance to the motion of bird bodies and wings, but affording more support. The largest and smallest birds would be
adversely affected, because of increased weight on the one
hand and of air resistance on the other, but the middle class
might remain as before, with some adjustment of muscle
and wing spread. The big change would be in insects. With
two or three times as great an atmospheric pressure, their
respiratory air tubes could carry oxygen to tissues to a
much greater distance. Denser, more supportive air would
require less effort to stay airborne, though it would di-
minish speed, and the respiratory system could work more
slowly. Insects consequently could in general be many
times larger than those we know and could be much more
formidable creatures for birds to prey on. Birds would
never have converted their original sharptoothed jaws into
fine-pointed beaks in this circumstance, and insects as certainly would have evolved much more dangerous equipment to ward off attack. The whole play becomes different.

Not only the play but the backdrop changes. There has
been an evolutionary interplay among insects and plants
as well. For time out of mind insects have been chewing

plant buds, especially those with stamens and seeds. Plants, being immobile, have always had the problem of transferring pollen from plant to plant, to ensure crossbreeding. Insects wandering from one to another have become agents in the process, though doing so for the sake of taste. The outcome is that brightly colored, strikingly patterned, well perfumed and flavored flowers have come into being as attractive but harmless lures for insects. If the size of insects had been much greater, flowers in general would have had to match them and for the most part would be like those flowers at present designed for birds and bats in place of insects—veritable giants of their kind.

Altogether such a large and heavy world would be more splashily colored and more animated in an aerial way. Plant and animal life on land would be thicker and shorter. Humans might exist in some admissible form. Through so dense an atmosphere they might never see the stars, while the light of the Sun and the Moon would be more diffuse. And land and sea would be so much more extensive that claustrophobia and the urge to get out into space would never arise.

Water, Water, Everywhere

ALMOST ALL SCIENCE FICTION that deals with other planets is concerned with pseudohumans and other creatures that live on land. They walk, run, crawl, even fly, and breathe air of sorts. Land is taken for granted and as a rule there seems to be little else. Here on Earth we also take land for granted and can hardly imagine things otherwise. The difficulty is real enough, for without land nothing remotely human could exist, and putting our own image completely out of the picture is not an appealing prospect. Yet the Earth's surface is three-quarters covered by oceans too salt for humans and other land animals to drink. In fact the origin of the light stuff that we call continents, sticking up from the Earth's crust, is a much-debated question, and scientists are much more in agreement when they discuss the origin of the water. So, picturing planets notably different from our own, suppose we do a thorough job and cover a planet completely with water. How salt such an ocean might be, we can leave aside for the present, though sea salt and salty blood and tears are by no means unconnected. The main question is, what kind of plant and animal life could evolve on a planet such as the Earth were it covered entirely with water, with no land in sight? Remember, this was one of the seriously considered possibilities for Venus until very recently.

In our present state of knowledge we have to assume the necessity for oxygen as well as water to underwrite animal life of any kind. The oceans of the Earth are well equipped in this respect, for whereas lakes may be stagnant and oxygen-deficient at the bottom, this is not the case for the seas and oceans. The Earth spins, and both its atmosphere and oceans are set in distinctive motions, with massive circulations that bring air and water into everchanging contact. Poles are cooler than the tropics and cooled water sinks, moves toward the equator, and there tends to rise again. Altogether the oceanic waters circulate roundabout and up and down, with the result that well-oxygenated water continually reaches even the greatest depths of the ocean basins. Marine animal life, much the same as the common kinds known in shallow seas, has been photographed at a depth of four miles on the floor of the abyss by means of the bathyscaphe. The whole of the oceans appears to be habitable by animal life, wherever sufficient food is available. Plant life is another matter, for plants, whether large and obvious seaweeds or in the form of single, microscopic cells, require light for photosynthesis and in consequence must live within the range of light penetration, no more than a few hundred feet from the surface at most.

The forms of life here on land are more familiar than is the life of the sea, yet the fundamental diversity of marine animal life far surpasses that of the land, including insects, although the reverse is true in the case of plants. Only two of the many basic kinds of animal life have made a notable success of living out of water, and some have not even managed to tolerate fresh-water in place of salt. The seas, if not actually the womb of life, are certainly the cradle. What lives beneath the surface?

Even a catalog of marine life would be overwhelming. At the most fundamental level, in the upper, light-struck layer of the ocean, single-cell plants in astronomical numbers constitute the pastures of the seas. In sheer aggregate bulk they amount to as much as all the vegetation on land. Seaweeds, whether attached near the shore or floating in the Sargasso Sea, add little to the whole. And directly or indirectly all the animal life of the sea depends on these dispersed, particulate, drifting minute forms of plant life. Even the life down below, inhabiting the miles of cold darkness, receives a manna from heaven in the form of the dead or decaying material sinking from the region of light —for most, a sort of catch-as-catch-can existence.

Fish and jellyfish are found at all levels, while starfish and sea pens are as much at home on the abyssal floor as they are on the shallow shelf near the shore. Perhaps the most fantastic of all creatures have yet to be caught, if we exclude the whales which we slaughter with little or no thought of their majesty and significance.

One kind are the giant squids. These are molluscs, as much so as any clam or snail, and closely related to the octopus. Small squid, one to two feet long, swarm in the seas in enormous schools, chasing and feeding on fish. Larger squid live at greater depths, where the great toothed whales dive to feed upon them. They rarely surface, having no need for atmospheric oxygen, and do not come within reach of man. Occasionally one is cast ashore by storm— with a twenty-foot-long body, ten-inch eyes, and thirty-foot tentacles equipped with innumerable three-inch suckers, a most formidable creature with a great beak to boot. Yet whales have been caught with sucker marks on their heads and beaks in their stomachs so large that their owners must have been several times the size of the giants we already know. The unseen drama in the depths surpasses anything that occurs on land, at least if we exclude man's own frantic actions and those of the long-extinct dinosaurian reptiles.

Another, possibly mythical, possibly not, is the sea serpent or what goes by this name. From time to time a report comes in of some enormous beast, usually seen in part only, that is unlike any creature known to biologists. In most cases the strangeness is simply the outcome of mistaken observation by untrained or unfamiliar individuals. Long ribbon fish or a squid out of place, for instance, seen not too clearly or far away, have undoubtedly been the basis for some sea serpent accounts. Yet when all is said something is left. Too many reports by ships' officers, and on one occasion by two zoologists, have been detailed, with too much in common, for them to be entirely disbelieved. The probability is that some large, powerful animal remains to be discovered, the nature of which we can only surmise, though various guesses have been made, such as a primitive, elongated whale, or an ichthyosaur left over from the Age of Reptiles.

This mystery of the deep inspired Murray Leinster, the science fiction writer, to write his story, "De Profundis," about an unknown intelligent creature of the abyss who knows nothing concerning what lies above the surface. Although the setting is here on this planet, with human intruders reaching the depth in a bathysphere, we can take the account as an imaginative exercise relevant to any water-covered planet. The chief actor is an imaginary creature that is never fully described, leaving the readers' own imagination something to work on, like a semi-abstract painting. It and its kind live on the sea bottom at a depth exceeding 18,000 feet, where pressure exceeds sixty times the atmospheric pressure at the Earth's surface, and where all is dark except for animal luminescence itself. The creature has tentacles, probably eight or ten since numbers one and seven are mentioned. They are exceedingly long, since at one point in the story a tentacle extends through the ocean surface while its owner is still three hundred feet below. And they are very sensitive to touch and can perceive differences in the solidity of rock and ooze.

An air bladder is present, serving to control the density of the animal as a whole so that it can float or drift at any level without exerting effort. There are eighty eyes, of an undescribed kind. And communication between one thinking monster and another, each inhabiting some submarine cave of its own, is by mental telepathy—complicated by the need to maintain a mental block concerning the location of the home site, since the creatures have a superb sense of space and a highly developed cannibalistic taste. Being cannibalistic, they can intermingle only during the breeding season when all appetite for food is absent.

Everything is experienced as from the bottom of that dark and dismal world, with some communal knowledge that light—of a monochrome blue—enters from far above, passing into the watery world from the Central Bubble of the Universe. Fierce, unbearable light enters the surface and only on occasion is a high-rising venture made. On such an ascent, and about 4,000 feet up from the abyss, all forms of life were seen to be smaller, with body lights less brilliant than those of the lesser creatures of the world below, and with a spatial sense that seemed to be imperfect.

This is an interesting portrayal in more ways than one—for what it is and what it isn't. Again the difficulty of imagining the unknown is evident, for the features described are recognizable. At the same time the author has avoided commitment to any more than is necessary and has fitted his creature as plausibly as possible to the chosen environment. The parts when assembled suggest something molluscan of supergiant size, combining the eight to ten flexible, manipulative tentacles of the octopus-squid group with the many-eyed visual system of the scallop, the only marine animal, molluscan or otherwise, that has so many eyes. The air bladder is taken over from the bony fish.

As portrayed, the creature combines characteristics of molluscs, fish, and humans, assuming that telepathic communication among human beings is fact and not entirely fancy. Yet the odds are very greatly against any such being existing in such a place except as the descendants of strays from some more congenial region. The large size is implausible simply on grounds of available food, for it must not be forgotten that all nutrient substance present in the ocean depths or on the abyssal floor itself, whether in living or no-longer-living form, is a direct or indirect product of the photosynthetic processes of the microscopic plant life near the surface. The living creatures of the great depths are characteristically small and relatively few and far between, though often of bizarre appearance. Yet they belong to the Earth as truly as we ourselves. They have merely taken a downward path whereas we and some others went up.

If we cease to regard the sea as merely the place where fish and other sea food come from, or as something to cross to reach another continent, we have only to penetrate its surface to enter a world as alien to ourselves as any strange planet would be. It is simple enough to do. Skin divers everywhere, complete with aqualung, explore safely to depths of one hundred feet or more—shallow enough in terms of the ocean depths, to be sure, but deep enough to open up a strange and beautiful universe cut off from the great atmospheric bubble by a glistening silver ceiling when looked at from below. Even this much of a dive is by no means necessary. All that is essential is to get in the water with face submerged, even if all you do is to stand on the bottom in four feet of water with a face mask and a snorkel to facilitate seeing and breathing. As far as you and the fish are concerned you share the same world.

The richest and most colorful part of this world is the coral reef fairyland of the tropics. The enchanting riot of color extends down to about twenty-five feet, but below that, even in the sun-blazed shallow coral seas, half of the real color goes, for light is filtered by the sea as though a rainbow were sinking through sieves of progressively finer mesh. At fifteen feet red turns to pink and at forty feet becomes black, and so does orange. At one hundred and twenty feet yellow starts turning green and all becomes a blue-green haze. At this depth no matter how much a coat of many colors a creature may wear, it is as drab as any other. Below this again, as depth passes to greater depth far beyond the range of unprotected diving men, the real twilight zone is reached where only a faint light glimmers overhead and all beneath is dark and cold.

All this is the Silent World of Jacques Cousteau, where sounds are rare and rarely heard. The only noisy creatures in the sea are mammals, either man himself with his ships and gear, or the true sea mammals such as whales and porpoise that have had a landed ancestry, for making noise and hearing it is mainly a product of the air.

Weight disappears when you enter the water. In fact you need a little extra to carry and keep you down. But pressure increases steadily and rapidly. On land a man bears an atmospheric pressure of several tons on the surface of his body without noticing it. Thirty-three feet down the pressure is doubled, at sixty-six it is tripled, and so on to the bottom thirty thousand feet below. Yet skin divers have swam without protection in pressures that would crack the hull of a submarine, for human tissue and all living tissue, being mostly water itself, is almost incompressible. The only weakness lies in the gas-filled lungs, although the solubility of gases in the blood is also a limiting factor for diving mammals. For those creatures that have no lungs there is no problem, and the tremendous pressure of the deep ocean might well be non-existent. Even the bony fish with their internal air bladder withstand the pressure well enough, in spite of the fact that the air bladder is a lung transformed and inherited from air-breathing freshwater fish of long ago; for gas pressure within the air bladder is made to counterbalance whatever pressure lies without.

This submarine world we are now beginning to know is of two kinds—a world of water in all directions, and one that has a solid or semisolid floor or side. In the first the effect of gravity must be neutralized. In the other, animals that would sink through water can find a lodging.

Submarine landscapes can be as weird and frightening as any that might be encountered elsewhere. On entering the water at the lonely island of Salvagem Grande, in the open Atlantic between Madeira and the Canaries, Cousteau and a companion experienced pure vertigo for the first time. They saw the bottom a hundred feet down in naked detail as though no water lay beneath them, empty of all specks of life or minerals—a horrible bright landscape with only empty space between them and the rocks below. Yet the sea supported them. And motionless barracudas and other fish hung suspended in the spell. "The weirdest realization was the bare glossy brown whorls of the lava slope, which felt polished to the touch. . . . On the submerged slope of the Salvagem Grande not one customary plant or animal appeared on the ghastly lava, save for one species that we almost ignored in disbelief. Along the cliff were immeasurable thousands of sea urchins, a large tropical variety with twelve-inch spines. We hung on our sides and stared at the clinging nation of urchins, moving their spines rhythmically like a field of wheat played by a breeze. We rolled back on our stomachs and felt the giddiness of the void. We were reassured to see our bubbles pluming toward the sky." Yet elsewhere, in the shallow tropic reefs, all is color and the branching forms of sea fans and sea coral, with the myriads of darting rainbow-colored fish that swim among them, and the plumed sea worms and sea anemones that are fastened to them, form a living forest that is animal through and through and as beautiful as any garden. It can sting and scratch for all that if you fail to keep your distance.

Again elsewhere, on the flat sandy floor along the coast of North Africa, a window opens onto another scene. Cousteau once more—"On the flat shallow floor northeast of Porquerollas we came upon an octopus city. We could hardly believe our eyes. Scientific credence, confirmed by our own experiences, holds that the octopus lives in crannies of rock and reef. Yet here were strange villas, indisputably erected by the octopi themselves. A typical home was one roofed with a flat stone two feet long and perhaps weighing twenty pounds. One side of the stone had been raised eight inches and propped by two lintels, a stone and a red building brick. The mud floor had been excavated five inches. In front of the lean-to was a wall of accumulated debris: crab and oyster shells, stones, shards of man-made pottery, sea anemones and urchins. A tentacle extended from the dwelling and curled around the rubble, and the owl-like eyes of the octopus peered at me over the wall. When I went closer, the tentacle contracted, sweeping debris up against the door, concealing the inhabitant." Evidently the octopus must be taken seriously.

Perhaps it was a scene such as this, together with the ease with which human beings can now explore the sea floor at depths down to a couple of hundred feet, that has led to the proposal, or prophesy, that before long we will establish submarine towns for our own habitation, beneath great plastic domes containing air, like olympic arenas. Overcrowding on land might one day tempt mankind to try such a venture, however ridiculous it appears to be at present. It might even be worth while for scientific reasons, though they are not evident at the moment. The significant point is that, given sufficient motive, such a project is entirely feasible, far more so in fact that putting and maintaining a similar outpost on the Moon. And not quite so likely to lead to madness.

The world of the greater depths is different. It has a bottom, a middle, and a top. The top is not the upper sunlit layer of drifting, swimming tumult but is the twilight zone where a little light has filtered, far too little for plant cells to go about their business. At the most, looking upward toward the sun at noon, all that could be seen would be the darker silhouettes of creatures shown against a blue-black background. It is not much, but enough for sensing prey. In various ways all mouths gape upward for the next meal from overhead. Yet somewhere in or close to this zone is the still mysterious, so-called deep-sea scattering layer where some small but numerous forms of marine life are so densely packed the layer sends back sound to the surface to echo-sounding ships. And it is here that fish and squid of various sizes descend to feed, with whales coming tumbling after.

In the lower twilight and farther down, however, life takes on another hue. Small fish and squid cruise horizontally at their selected and accommodated level, yet all the time gazing upward with everted, telescopic eyes. Others again have light-organs on their head and sides, of various color and arrangement, like ships that move at night and need to declare their position and direction. These seem to serve to keep scattered communities together, necessary for breeding and perhaps for a little needed sociability. Such as these have, for their size, large, saucer-like eyes, properly set, which gather even the faintest living glow of a fellow creature, whether friend or foe.

Finding food of a suitable kind is the problem and deep-sea fish, squid, and shrimp are known that lure light-attracted prey to themselves by emitting living light. Another creature as fantastic as any is not exactly an octopus or a squid but somewhere in between. It is also in between in another sense, for it spends its life suspended in a layer of oceanic water roughly six thousand feet from the ocean floor and at a greater but variable distance from the surface —in complete darkness, without lights, in ice-cold water, and probably as near motionless as can be—the most watery of its kind, with the transparent texture of a jelly-fish, with eight arms spread akimbo and a pair of little tentacles for handling the delicate living morsels that come its way. This is the real inhabitant of the abyss, rather than the giant of fiction.

Finally, on the floor itself, except where the great mid-oceanic ridges mount halfway to the surface, spilling lava down their sides, there is only the deep sea ooze of unknown depth and tremendous age. Few things find a foot-

ing in it—stalked sponges, sea squirts and luminescent sea
pens. Worms and such burrow within it, and starfish and
long spined urchins lie upon it. All are apparently comparative newcomers descended from shallower regions—
not primeval kinds at all. The great bulk of marine life
and most of its variety remains where food is most abundant—the uppermost layer of the open ocean for those that
can keep themselves from sinking, and the shallow shelves
of continents and islands for those that cannot. Such is the
unfamiliar world close at hand, hidden by water and now
alien to us because in ancestral form we left it so long ago.

On a planet similar to the Earth in every way except that
the whole globe is covered by an ocean several miles deep,
what could we expect? How much of what now inhabits
the oceans of the Earth has to be subtracted because land in
some way has played an essential role in its creation? It is a
goodly amount and by far the most. To get the answer we
have to see another world that is not in outer space nor
beneath the surface of the sea but far away in past time,
and at different times.

The Earth at present is cooler than through most of past
time, has much more extensive land surfaces, and is in
a comparatively mountainous state. Yet there was a time
when little dry land stood above the surface of the water.
For most of known geological history, the greater part of
the continental surfaces has been covered by so-called epicontinental seas of no more than several hundred feet in
depth. As the Earth convulsed during one period of moun-
tain-building and ocean-basin-deepening after another,
these shallow seas came and went in somewhat regular
manner. When fully present they were enormous, in North
America, for instance, extending from the Sierras to the
Appalachians and from the Gulf of Mexico to the Arctic
Sea, and to a comparable extent elsewhere, covering such

presently elevated regions as the Himalayas and the Andes. Their importance in the scheme of things was that the submerged continental surfaces supplied a solid platform within the striking distance of the light entering the sea surface—forming extensive sea floors where marine life could flourish in the presence of abundant food and where it was no longer necessary to maintain a density no greater than sea water. Marine creatures could sink with impunity and not only rest their possibly overgrown and over-weighted bodies on the bottom but could indulge in growing heavy protective calcareous shells, a luxury denied those that had to keep up in the world at all costs. Here evolved the clams, snails, and the great shelled ancestors of the octopus and squid, together with the sea urbins, star-fish, not to mention crustaceans too heavy to maintain a swimming existence. These comprise three of the major groups of marine animals. The great squid of the open seas and deep ocean are descendants, and so are most of the creatures found on the abyssal floor. Eliminate the submerged continental platforms, and most of this display of marine life never comes into being.

Yet this is but half of it. Apart from the big squid, the seas are dominated by fish and sea mammals, and at one time fish-shaped sea reptiles, now extinct. Marine fish are descendants of freshwater ancestors. The reptiles and mammals are primitively land-based quadrupeds, and their marine representatives are all creatures that have become modified for life in water. Remove the land, and these all go too.

Something is left, naturally, but only that which could evolve in the open ocean within range of light, where only death awaited any that sank below. It is little enough—comb jellies, so-called, and perhaps jellyfish, though this is not certain; small, swimming crustaceans perhaps and some transparent arrow worms; but mainly the single-celled plant life and inconspicuous creatures that feed upon it. If such would have been the case on this planet, had there been no land, what reason have we to expect any better of any other landless though watery world?

N I N E

Great Expectations

IF WE OR OUR DESCENDANTS should journey beyond Sirius and make a landing on some more or less congenial planet not unlike the Earth in its place in the Sun and in its quota of land and ocean, what would our expectations be? We might, just might, find beings suggestively human, though we certainly should not expect to. At the other end of the scale, what little can we expect? Will life inevitably be present as plant and animal? Something akin to plant life must certainly be present, but do the more animated and dependent forms of life necessarily accompany it? And if so, would we also necessarily recognize the animal life for what it is? How inevitable are heads and tails? Must there be eyes and brains? In how much of a rut does Creation move?

The Earth remains our model. Life that has been inevitable here should be inevitable elsewhere where conditions have been the same. Even if the basic mixture was a little different and the oven of another sun somewhat faster or slower, the bread of life should still come out in a more or less familiar form. It would depend upon its sun for future life as fully as it does here, forever building up itself out of the most available and lightest materials, with the local solar radiation supplying the power. It would have to be photosynthetic, and sooner or later units of life comparable to the living cells of Earthly organisms would come into being within the liquid matrix of any well-born planet's watery envelope. No detail might be the same, but the unremiting pressure to become self-maintaining, self-producing, and self-reproducing would be so remorseless that living creations with the essence of cells could not fail to appear. Wherever a star shines upon its planets, if life be possible it will be driven into being.

The next step is equally inevitable, assuming that Nature is herself no matter where and that she can neither leave well enough alone nor continue forever without making seemingly inspired mistakes. In an inconceivably vast population of independent cell-like organisms, all busily reduplicating themselves, some will do so incompletely and remain joined together like Siamese twins. If this should be an inheritable form of imperfect accomplishment, then conjoined, multicellular masses of cells would come into existence and some of these would perpetuate their kind as multicellular organisms. What molds can they be placed in?

Suppose we start with the plants. By far the greater part of evolutionary time on Earth has been devoted to aquatic life, both freshwater and marine. And by far the bulk of this life, when added together, is still in the form of innumerable independent cells invisible to the naked eye except for the greenish tinge they give to the water. Some kinds are multicellular filaments, others form broader but paper-thin sheets. Everything they need is around them—water, minerals, and the pervading light—while gravity hardly counts. As long as the cells are exposed to the water little else matters, and photosynthetic cells in the water of another planet would have no occasion to do more than is the custom here.

For land to be colonized, any plantlike organisms would have to meet the same basic requirements as on Earth. They would have to contend with gravity and cope with a drastic change concerning their water supply. On any planet anywhere in the universe, all organisms, whether definable as plant or animal or something else, have to adapt to these two physical conditions if emergence from water is to be accomplished. One way of contending with gravity it to give in to it—as in Bernard Shaw's policy for getting rid of temptation—and lichens and some other lowly plants of the Earth lie flat against the ground, turning gravity to good effect. Growth, however, whether of individuals or populations, is then limited to the two-dimensional world of flatland. Where competition for space exists it seems again inevitable that some kinds of plant life would rise up, necessitating a strengthening of the conjoined walls of the supporting cells. Plants here have cell walls greatly strengthened and thickened by layers of cellulose, lignin, or other organic fibers, which also serve to seal the water in. Some similar material, constructed from hydrogen and carbon at least, and probably oxygen, would surely be produced to serve the same purpose for plants out of water wherever in the universe they may occur.

Given this much, the need to raise the photosynthetic factory of the plant toward the light, the need to send growth processes downward into rock or soil to reach water, the need to support the crown against the pull of gravity, the need to conduct liquid from top to bottom and from bottom to top, are all such fixed constructional engineering requirements that the system of root-stem-leaftop, with all manner of variation, must be virtually universal.

Plant life elsewhere would undoubtedly look strange, but should be recognizable for what it is. That it should be green is another matter. There are chemical reasons why chlorophyll is green, and there is no doubt that chlorophyll works most effectively. But it appears green because it reflects green light without using it and this seems strange, for it amounts to a rejection of the main part of visible light and of the greatest source of energy. Obviously this is the dominant form of photosynthesis here on Earth, but there are also those photosynthetic bacteria which are not green at all but are purple. Plant life on other planets may well be any color except green, and vegetation-covered landscapes and even much of the seas might have a purple or an orange hue.

As for animal life, we have to proceed with caution. One might say that everyone knows what an animal is and could make no mistake. Yet that itself would be a mistake even here, for there are many forms of truly animal life which seemed much more plant-like than animal to the early naturalists who first observed them. There is no need here to go into the list and one of them, the sponges, will suffice. Sponges, including the old-fashioned bath sponge, which was the horny skeleton of a sponge, are animals that look like plants. Mostly marine, they all spend their lives immovably attached to some solid object and there grow until they die. Along the shore where they are exposed to surf they typically grow as spreading, encrusting spongy stuff, of any color under the sun, and showing no more sign of animated life than a cabbage. In quieter waters they usually have the shape of a vase, with or without a stalk. Yet they have no chlorophyll, do not photosynthesize their own substance, but filter the surrounding water through the finest of living sieves and sustain themselves on the microscopic organisms contained therein. They are vegetative, but are not plants. Some can even propagate vegetatively, as can quite a few other kinds of lowly animal life. Yet we have to admit them to the animal kingdom though they be without muscles, gut, and nerves of any kind, let alone anything to see with, think with, or by which to move about. Could such as these exist elsewhere? They represent a way of life, the opportunity would occur, and if Nature evolving on Mother Earth is typical of her kind, it would be taken.

Leaving sponges aside, most kinds of Earthly animal life, starting with those that live in water, have patterns of two radically different kinds—those with radial and those with bilateral symmetry. In fact a century ago the animal kingdom was divided into these two categories, before it was realized that these two types of organization have been imposed time and again by worldly circumstances and tell little concerning the relationship of one kind of animal to another. They represent two ways of life for animals, whether they live in water or any other fluid on any planet anywhere. They represent two fundamentally different ways of fitting structure to circumstance, and the choice is open to all.

The only assumptions we need to make are that the individual animals are at least large enough to be seen, that they live in water, and that they must obtain food from their surroundings. Animals on land need to be considered separately and as emigrants from the water. These assumptions should be valid on any planet where animal life exists, using the term animal life to mean life which requires the substance of other forms of life as food. For the animal life concerned, food is the problem. And as in the case of all problems of this kind facing living organisms, only a limited number of biological engineering solutions are possible.

This is one of the most fundamental principles behind

the whole course of evolution of animals and plants during the last billion years on Earth. It is the reason why so many more or less unrelated kinds of animal life come up with the same inventions, such as legs, camera-type eyes, or red, oxygen-carrying hemoglobin. Evolution, in spite of its appearance of having direction, is generally said to be the result of pure chance—that is to say, variation among the offspring of any particular kind of organism is haphazard and to some extent in all directions, and the process of natural selection is merely the circumstances which enable this or that sort to survive and propagate in turn more readily than the rest. If this were all, it is difficult to see how such progression from fish to reptile to mammal to man, for instance, could have come about. The explanation seems to lie in the limitation in the number of possible paths leading to the solution of any biological need. To put it another way, it is as though the active evolutionary force is a boy with a shotgun and unlimited ammunition, firing continually in all directions, but adjacent to a house with a limited number of windows. Blind chance operates through the boy, but sooner or later every pane will have been broken and the shot that enters will have telling effect. Given time enough, and time there has been aplenty, the living stuff of a planet will find all the openings available for an evolutionary breakthrough.

So in this business of feeding. Water can be sifted for the minute food organisms in suspension; various forms of living sieves are possible, of which the sponge is one example and the oyster is another. Relatively large volumes of water must be passed through or over the tissues if a fair living is to be made, with a minimum of exertion and usually no form of locomotion.

Another solution, which also reduces exertion to a minimum and therefore the amount of sustenance necessary, is to stand and wait, or drift and wait, and always be ready to seize any hapless creature that blunders into too-close range. A sea anemone does this, and consists of little more than a sac attached to the sea floor by its blind end, with its open, mouth end facing outward or upward. Jellyfish are essentially similar, but drifting in the water with mouth opening downward. In both cases their world is up and down and all around. As long as one remains attached and the other stays aloft, it makes no difference how much each turns around. Food can come from any point of the compass and one side is like another. Tentacles accordingly reach out in all directions, as spokes of a wheel of which the hub is the mouth. Radial symmetry is the only logical solution when living food arrives unbidden from all sides, and it is likely to be a universal answer.

Centrally placed bodies with tentacles arranged regularly around the circumference at the mouth end is a simple and clearly successful organization for obtaining a livelihood. Yet insofar as the underlying principle is to stay put, either attached to some sort of solidity or drifting with but not within an ocean current, little is required except the capacity to respond to touch and to seize whatever food organisms come into contact. Nervous systems are at a minimum and brains, however lowly, are absent. A means of livelihood, taken alone, can be a very drab life.

Jack London once wrote that the ideal existence is a jellyfish floating in a tideless, tepid, twilight sea. All to one's own taste. This ideal, however, may better apply to the sea anemone sitting motionless on its base on the bottom of the sea, for the jellyfish actually has rather more to do and cannot relax with such impunity. It must keep within a certain distance of the surface, and its bell-shaped body rhythmically pulsates in the process of so doing. But to do so effectively, the body needs to be sensitively responsive to either the force of gravity pulling downward or the stimulus of light entering the water from above. Accordingly, some have gravity-sensitive organs around their rim, some have light-sensitive organs similarly located, and some have both. To keep a place in the world it seems necessary either to be glued to a spot, in which case the spot has to be the right one from the start, or else to have the means to move and senses to make the movements serve the right end. The cosmic forces of light and gravity supply the cues, and even the radiate jellyfish has to respond to them.

Yet the radiate pattern leads nowhere in particular. All points of the compass are the same, and even a crawling starfish sets off in any chosen direction by leading with the ray that lies that way. To change direction it simply stops and sets off in another, without turning around. No wonder when it cannot tell which way its head should be it goes without a head. Lumping them together, the anemones, jellyfish, starfish and their like, we see a collection of ornamental creatures of beautiful form and symmetry, but none with a brain and all with a destiny long ago attained. The pattern and plan of action are simple enough, and must be open to the evolving aquatic animal life of any planet.

The third blueprint for living construction involves both symmetry and system. The system is a tube within a tube, with one end always foremost and the other behind, food being processed in a sort of assembly-line manner within the inner tube, though disassembly would be closer to the mark. In its bare essentials the whole thing is an exceedingly simple and effective device that would inevitably be discovered by enterprising life anywhere—an outer tube-like body which moves forward through the liquid world external to it, and an inner tube through which the food-containing fluid flows. In more or less elaborate form it is typical not only of worms but of mice and men.

Moving forever forward, not in any particular compass direction but in the sense of following one's nose, means heads and tails. And effective progression generally requires keeping an even keel, either in the water or gliding on the ground, for otherwise there is wasted motion. This is the key to the pattern that most animals possess, which is bilateral symmetry. To have a head and a tail representing two ends of a body; a left and a right side which mirror one another—the fearful symmetry of the tiger of William Blake—and an upper and a lower surface; these are features that characterize most creatures and are too easily taken for granted.

Head ends lead to heads, and a pair of symmetrical sides lead to a symmetrical pairing of other features, from sense organs to appendages for locomotion. Only in the middle line do things remain unpaired. How important all this is you can see for yourself, for in a way this could be the laying of the groundwork for a human being and any departure from the lines so far would lead to a travesty of the human form. Even a ship at sea must conform to this, with a fore and aft and port and starboard, let alone a deck and keel. These are requirements for a moving but stable body whether living or not, and we should expect to find them everywhere.

There must be limits to strangeness, and it may be comforting to feel that life on distant planets may turn out to be not too unlike our own, though wishful thinking here may be playing too great a part. J. B. S. Haldane long ago expressed his suspicion "that the universe is not only queerer than we suppose, but queerer than we *can* suppose," meaning that human beings have a particular kind of mind which can think well in certain ways but only in certain ways, and our most serious limitations are those we cannot discern. However this may be, all that can be done is to try to recognize a mental brick wall if we come up against one. Meanwhile there is no alternative but to proceed from the known to the unknown, to sift the universal rules from the special, and continue to examine the life we know for all its worth.

The head end of an animal carries the primary organs of sense, since it is better to see where you are going than where you have been. Navigation, whether toward the stars, a meal, or the opposite sex, is based on appreciation at a distance, and awareness of things at a distance is based on sensitivity to cosmic and chemical agents. Yet this sensitivity is not something that has come into being here because animals needed eyes, ears, and nose, but as a development of a fundamental sensitivity of all living protoplasm to virtually all the forces in its environment.

This is another fact of the utmost importance, for if this pervading sensitivity evolved as a quality of the Earth's evolving primeval life itself, in response to everything about it, then we can expect that wherever life has evolved throughout the universe, a similar sensitivity will be incorporated. More than anything else, perhaps, this quality is what we recognize and mean when we speak of life; it is the difference between the quick and the dead. For the stuff of all living things is sensitive and responsive to light and other radiation, to touch, to all manner of chemicals, to the impact of sound waves and, more indirectly, to the pull of gravity. It is out of the general that the particular has arisen, in the form of many kinds of organs for vision, taste, smell, balance, touch, and hearing. And they have arisen where they serve their purpose best, commonly but not invariably on the front end of an animal where they help make a head.

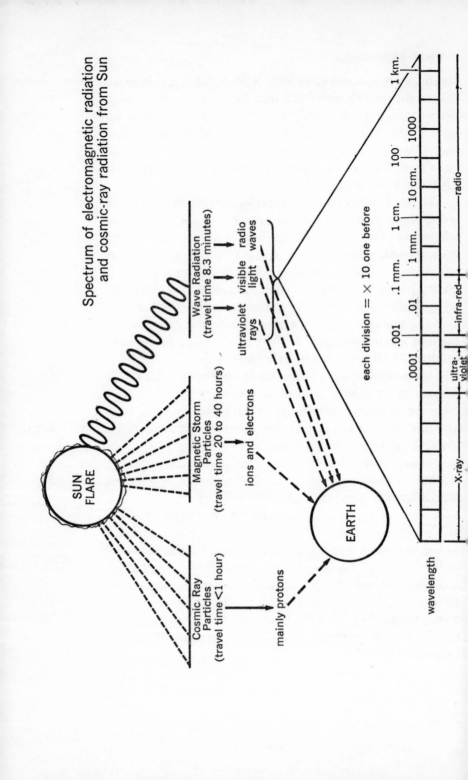

Spectrum of electromagnetic radiation
and cosmic-ray radiation from Sun

This is basic biology of an Earthly kind, though still a necessary base to build on. To begin with, sense organs are constructed of cells as building blocks, though cells with exceptionally sensitive surface structures. The simplest organs are those that serve such senses as smell and taste, where all that is needed are local congregations of the cells in question, for chemical influences come directly to the living threshold and are remarkably effective. Light rays on the other hand must be concentrated, and several kinds of eyes, each with its own particular sort of lens and retinal apparatus, have come into existence for this purpose, in many cases to form an image. Gravity is generally sensed by having small, heavy granules present within a cavity lined by sensitive cells, where changes in the position of the weights convey information about the position of the body in space. Whatever kind of inner world is built up within the organism depends on the variety and general nature of these sensory organs, as the blind and the deaf among us know only too well.

It is remarkable how often the same device turns up among unrelated kinds of animals. The gravity-sensitive balancing organ is essentially the same in forms as remote from one another as jellyfish, shrimp, octopus, and the whole group of backboned animals from fish to man. Its simplicity and effectiveness make it readily acquired and in any case how else can a generally weightless organism, in water, become aware of gravity except by having a little weight locally that is heavier than water? The only related device concerns not the force of gravity itself but the centrifugal force associated with sudden turning movements of a body or head.

Backboned creatures, in or out of water, have three fluid-filled canals in each inner ear, joined to the central gravity-sensitive organ, representing the three planes of three-dimensional space and serving to record movements in those planes. But so does the octopus, at least in an equivalent form, and this in spite of the fact that the two types of animal have undoubtedly evolved these organs independently of one another. They have discovered the same engineering solution to the problem of analyzing their own motion in space, and at least for aquatic animals there appears to be no other. It is simply a matter of locating sensitive cells where they can feel the relative movement of a fluid along a solid surface—as in a rotating glass of water where the glass turns but the water remains stationary or lags behind. Creatures on other planets may have other more or less living material at their disposal, but in the face of a general need to know how they are moving and turning within their natural medium, these are the devices most likely to evolve. When only one exit exists, all must go that way or remain confined.

And so with eyes. An eye, so-called, may serve merely as a light-sensitive organ capable only of giving direction, or it may in addition to this form a detailed image of external things. Even the simplest of free-moving organisms, such as many single-celled plants, have an eye-spot that serves the basic function; most lowly and larval kinds of animals have one or more simple eyes that are little better, though they are larger and are multicellular. As a rule they consist of a minute cup of light-sensitive cells, backed by dark pigment to prevent light from reaching them except through a cuticular lens that fills the cup. Such as these are invaluable for sensing the direction of a source of light, and few motile animals do without unless they have already done better. And again, how else could such simple eyes be constructed? Only irrelevant variations of the lens-cup-pigment combination seem to be possible, although great improvement can always be made.

One of the most startling parallels in the animal kingdom is the amazing similarity of the eyes of the most advanced octopus-type molluscs on the one hand and the eyes of vertebrates on the other. The two groups of animals are as unrelated as it is possible to be, yet each has produced the perfect camera eye complete with lens, retina, pigment layer, focusing muscles, iris diaphragm, transparent cornea, supporting wall structure, and lids. There are differences in fine detail and in construction procedure, as might be expected, but in all essentials they are the same. Yet the reason for all this is clear. It is simply that, so far as human ingenuity is concerned, a good camera has to be constructed according to a certain basic specification, and what we have to do with film and metal and glass, animals have had to do with their own living substance, or be satisfied with less.

Starting with the simplest of eyes, however, there are two roads to follow, one leading to the bigger and better camera-type eye by a process of enlargement and elaboration, and the other to the compound eye of insects, spiders, and crustaceans, consisting of a large number of slender, independent eye units which together form a crude image but are marvelously effective for detecting movement. No other kinds of eyes have evolved on Earth, although both kinds have evolved a number of times. Living matter is versatile and malleable, but the formation of sharply focused and intensity-controlled images is determined by the behavior of light and the rules of optics which are the same anywhere, whether life is present and involved, or not.

Assuming therefore that eyes evolve wherever animal life has been in existence for a sufficient length of time, what are the chances that eyes will be present as a single pair located on a head? The probability can be estimated only by looking at some of our terrestrial colleagues. Who has one eye, who has two, and who has a multiplicity?

The only place for a solitary Cyclopean eye seems to be on the front or the top of the head, in the middle line. As a rule such eyes are simple, merely aiding the owner to move toward or away from a source of light, and occur mostly in creatures verging on the microscopic. However, scorpions and so-called water fleas, which are crustaceans, possess a pair of compound eyes so closely fused together that they appear as one. Otherwise the single median eye turns up only in abnormal development, or else as an experimentally produced single-eyed fish fry or frog tadpole capable of swimming about but apparently not able to survive in a competitive world. Obviously median camera-type eyes can almost too readily be produced. They are apparently not countenanced because of either of two liabilities. Where eyes belong in the front of the face, as in man, ape, and monkey, for direct, stereoscopic vision ahead, two eyes are necessary for vision in depth. You have only to drive a car in traffic with one eye covered to find out how expensively handicapped you are. And if eyes are necessary for panoramic views of either side, the field of vision of the single eye is dangerously restricted.

On the other hand, two eyes in front, whether the camera eyes of a man or an owl, or the compound eyes of a dragonfly, or the simple eyes of marine worms, serve well either for estimation of distance or to keep the body moving on a steady course. By the same token a pair of organs for smell or hearing can determine direction when one cannot. Two is so often the right number, when one is inadequate and three is a crowd.

Very few animals in fact have more than a pair of symmetrically placed eyes, and even among these the scallop is exceptional—for here the hundreds of small, beautifully constructed eyes along the edges of the mantle are merely designed to detect the movement of an approaching starfish coming from almost any direction. They simply trigger an escape reaction, and have nothing to do with a brain. The only creature with a battery of eyes that operate through a brain worthy of the name is the spider. Spiders have eight compound eyes of a mediocre sort which are grouped together on the top of the head, somewhat like turrets. The rear pair serve to watch behind for either food or danger. The other three pairs work together but in succession. If something comes within the range of vision of one of the outermost pair, the head turns until the object is brought into the field of the two pairs of eyes in the middle, and the spider then advances. When the object is brought into focus of the forward pair, the spider jumps to attack. The whole business is much like a self-operated mechanism with seeing instruments, and the eight eyes together do not compare with the camera or the compound eye of a bird or a bee. Accordingly, we settle for two eyes, as well as two ears and two organs for smell, in fact two of everything that relates to things at a distance. If ever we should meet an intelligent being on another planet or even see his picture through interplanetary, intragalactic television, we should at least recognize what passes for his face and expect to see two of everything except the mouth.

The mouth itself, of course, might be farther down on the underside, as it is in spiders, scorpions, and some other creatures. And taste, which is concerned only with chemicals already in contact with the body, may be all over the place and by no means confined to the inside of the mouth and to the tongue, if tongue there be. Among Earthly creatures the catfish of muddy rivers not only has taste-bud-covered filaments drooping from the lower lip, for dangling along the bottom in a drooly sort of way, but has taste buds all along the sides of its body as well. A tasty morsel near the base of its tail registers immediately, and the head turns back at once to reach it. A gluttonous state such as this is only possible, however, in connection with a naturally wet skin, and even then it seems to be compensation for living in a liquid smog.

Just as the fundamental rules of physical construction determine how organs such as eyes and ears are formed, so the inherent qualities of liquid, solid, or gaseous states determine the shape of bodies that travel through them. Living bodies take the shape that offers least resistance to the surrounding medium. For speed in water the shape of a fish is mandatory. Fish have it, squid have it, seals have it, penguins have it, porpoises and whales have it, submarines have it, the submerged part of a ship has it, and so did the extinct reptiles known as ichthyosaurs. There is no escape. It is as though one shape and one shape only can move rapidly through water with a minimum of resistance and creation of turbulence, and that all living things that do so move have been poured into the same mold. Whether or not water is the only liquid medium supporting life in the universe is beside the point. Forced movement through any liquid calls for the same basic shape, and fishlike bodies must be a universal commonplace.

How big such a body can be is another matter. In water, where gravity only affects things that are heavier or lighter than water and the problem of motion is to slip through the viscous fluid, the upper limit for size turns on a matter of solid geometry concerning the living object as such. It is the old question of surface and volume, something that has entered into every detail of construction of ourselves and all else that lives. Take a sphere, for instance. If you double its width you have cubed its contents but only squared its surface area. If the sphere were a living cell through whose surface everything must enter or leave, the larger it becomes the less the surface available to a certain mass of contained living matter. One consequence is that cells remain microscopic, each with a maximum surface relative to its contents, and mice and elephants differ in the number of their cells rather than in cell size. It also follows that as animals increase in bulk and their cells reach astronomical numbers—more than ten thousand billion nerve cells in the human brain alone—the question of supply and demand, when supply is limited by surfaces and demand depends on volume, becomes crucial.

Lung surfaces become exceedingly expanded, though packed within the chest; digestive tubes become many times as long as the body, but coiled within it and with an infinitely folded inner lining; within its limiting chamber the heart works ever harder to pump blood fast enough through increasingly branching vessels to supply the muscles and other tissues. With every increase in size, the strain of merely keeping the body and brain in the manner to which they have been accustomed grows greater. Every mechanical and biological device to improve efficiency and reduce expenditure gets called on until at last the limit is reached at which Nature herself must call a halt. On this Earth she stopped when she made the greatest of the whales some time ago—two-ton, twenty-foot babies in nine months that become one hundred and twenty tons with a hundred-foot length when fully grown—as much living matter as can be kept together in a healthy state inside a single skin. From what we know of the whale and its supply of food, no more can be expected, and if life on other planets can do as well it will have done marvelously indeed.

The shape and size of living things, the design of the most intricate and precise of special organs, the distributive maintenance systems of bodies, are all governed by the laws of energy and matter. Opportunity varies with circumstance, but when opportunities call the answers are made according to universal law. Every planet capable of bearing life can play the game, each with its own set of dice but governed by the rules. The chances are that on favored planets we would find life much to our liking, if not in our like.

Landed Gentry

BORN IN THE PRIMORDIAL SOUP, nurtured in waters salt and fresh, most kinds of animal life remain submerged. Only the adventurous few have wriggled or crawled or clambered onto the dry continental platforms of the Earth. For those that have done so it has meant giving up the tasty salts of the sea and exchanging too much water for too little. For the earthy and sluggish kinds this has been the main sacrifice, but for others the newly felt pull of gravity has stood them on their toes. Remodeling is always a tricky business, and the history of land- and airborne creatures is somewhat as though a submarine had been taken from the water and converted to rushing about on land and later to entering the air as a flying machine. This is a very different matter from designing automobiles and airships from scratch, yet it is the only way when the original constructions have had to be made under water. The engineering possibilities and restrictions are primarily those presented or imposed by the physical environment in each place and by the rules of conversion of use in different circumstances. Passage from water to out-of-water and the different conditions for motion through water, on dry land, and through atmosphere must present the same difficulties and challenge for life on any planet with land, sea, and air capable of supporting life. The keys to success here are the keys to success anywhere, at least in principle, and there have been enough cases of successful remodeling for us to see who have and who have not managed to do this and, in the case of the successful ones, by what means.

As in remodeling anything, that which is to be remodeled must be at least somewhat suitable for the new use. The horse-drawn carriage was converted into the early automobile by substituting an engine for the horse—the carriage was in a way preadapted for the new employment and the subsequent changes for the most part have left the basic structure as it was. This is very different from making machineguns instead of typewriters, when all must be redesigned from the beginning. Thus animals that have left the water for active life on land have had to be fairly well equipped to do so before they ever emerged. This has been called preadaptation, but it does not imply any anticipation of a change of life. No creature can adjust to living on land if it cannot tolerate living out of water for at least a short while. If there is real advantage in remaining on land, then of those that stay awhile Nature will favor those that can stay longest and their progeny will likely outnumber the others, and so it goes.

Living out of water is a feat for any water-sodden representative of life and, except where atmospheric humidity is maximum, requires an outer surface capable of conserving the body water within. The backboned quadrupeds, all descendants of early fish, have an outer coat of keratin, in the form of scales, feathers, hair, and skin, which is a protein substance that serves this waterproofing purpose, carried over from aquatic ancestors. Insects, spiders, scorpions, centipedes, millipedes, and even the lowly earthworm have an external coat with similar properties, but of a different substance called chitin, also an inheritance from aquatic ancestors. Snails brought their shells ashore and withdraw into them when air gets too dry. The remodeling to make a frog takes place during the growth of every individual, and is a spectacular transformation from what is essentially fish to air-breathing, land-jumping acrobats.

There are two paths to the land from the salt sea cradle —the direct route ashore from the sea, which seems to be the route the land crabs and snails have taken, and the more roundabout journey by way of fresh water, the route of the remainder. The latter way is less abrupt for creatures that have come out of the sea and carry sea salt in their veins and tissues. Passing through fresh water with a sojourn of a hundred million years or more permitted the adventurers from the sea to adjust their tissues to lack of salts, with their body fluids and tissues a salty compromise of sea salts diluted to one third. Even then the freshwater fishes had to work hard to maintain as high a content as this. Their kidneys are forever pumping out the water that continually seeps in and dilutes their salts. Otherwise they would become too waterlogged to live. This has been a necessary process for survival in fresh water, but the water-pumping mechanism of the kidneys became a liability out of water. Since the machinery couldn't be stopped it had to be counteracted, and land vertebrates, including man, have kidney units that filter water out of the bloodstream as fast as ever but have other kidney tissue which then draws most of it back again, a case of remodeling twice over. The whole story is told at length in Homer Smith's *From Fish to Philosopher.*

The primary accommodation to life out of water is physiological—to retain sufficient body water, though forever changing it; to keep enough salts in solution and in much the same ratio as they occur in the sea; and to absorb oxygen from air instead of water. Unless these conditions have been met, nothing further is possible. As a matter of fossil fact those fish whose descendants became land-lubbers under other names were well equipped with air-breathing lungs, as well as gills, while still the inhabitants of water, though admittedly of water of a somewhat swampy sort.

Let us then look for a moment at two major kinds of animals that have remained exclusively marine. One of the most striking, widely distributed, and populous groups in the sea are the echinoderms—spiny-skinned creatures—a group which includes starfish, sea urchins, and others. None is even estuarine, let alone in good fresh water or on land. Their dependency is not merely water but the full salt solution that is sea water, for they all have a unique hydraulic system of internal tubes through which sea water is forced, usually to operate a peculiar locomotory apparatus. The sea is so much a part of their interior that they cannot do without. Fresh water kills at once and they have never entered it.

The other is the group of cephalopod molluscs—the octopus, squid, and others—which have probably ignored freshwater situations because they found much better fishing in their marine homeland. Squid are fast swimmers above all else and for the most part shun even the shore of the oceans, but the octopus lives along the shore and can easily maneuver itself out of water over the ground, though not for long. There is a story of one that escaped from an aquarium in a private library and rushed arm over arm over arm up and down the book shelves, scattering books far and wide. Such a creature might have been a great success on land and perhaps a formidable competitor with vertebrates, if only it had a more impermeable hide. As things are, the octopus and its kind are naked-skinned to an extreme, with an integument exceedingly sensitive, and watery through and through. An hour out of water and an octopus is already on the way to becoming a mummy.

A body out of water needs to be moved, and under its own power. A lump of a creature that could not move at all on land would never have gotten out of water in the first place. No amount of waving a fishy tail from side to side in the insubstantial air has ever moved a fish along, though in contact with the ground the long, sinuous body of an eel can wriggle forward almost as though swimming in water. Quadruped progression, with right forefoot and left rearfoot moving forward alternately with left forefoot and right rearfoot, began with early fish using their rather muscular fins to push the ground-resting body along. Fins became legs—another case of characteristic remodeling. But tails became unemployed except as counterweights for heads, as flywhisks for those that cannot swat, or as a hidden basal reinforcement for up-ended men and apes.

To remodel a fish into a four-footed creature supporting its own weight and capable of ambling about on land, breathing air, and remaining fairly safe from dessication calls for a time and place suitable for such a project. The Earth as it is now, even without man around to monkey with it, seems to offer little or no encouragement to anything of the sort. In any case the actual Earthly event took place long ago when the relationship of land and water, leaving the sea aside, was as different as possible from present conditions. The time—from two to three hundred million years ago during the periods of coal forest formation. The place—the margins of shallow lakes and swamps, bordering soggy lands that nowhere rose more than a foot or so above the water level; with so much water everywhere

evaporating from the surface and actively being passed into
the atmosphere through vegetation, humidity was continuously as high as it could be. During these geological
periods, the Carboniferous particularly, there was little
difference between being in or out of water except for the
effect of gravity on body weight. On the continental stage
where the event was taking place, the world stayed wet and
fresh no matter where one went. Without such a world,
enduring for so long a time, it is unlikely that fish could
ever have made the grade, and Earth would have lacked
its beasts of the fields, birds of the air, and masterminding
men. How probable comparable conditions might arise or
have arisen on planets in other solar systems is the question. At least we know that the Earth as it is at present is
in an unusual state, in having high mountain ranges, and
an Ice Age as well, and the more favorable circumstances
are much the more likely.

Legs have ruled the drier terrestrial scene during all the
time it has taken old original four-legs to turn into cheese-
cake. Four legs have mostly remained four legs, and the
only reduction is seen in certain lizards of long ago, in all
birds, and in apes and men. Two is the absolute minimum
—a pogo stick is an exclusively human invention incompatible with bones and sinews. So is a wheel. When
traveling abroad, should we therefore expect to find the
land-living inhabitants, with whom we might hope to communicate, walking on two legs or four, or running around
like a centipede concentrating on which of a score of legs
to put down next?

The answer can be pieced together from what we know
of the lesser fry, rather than from vertebrates with no more
than two pairs of legs to start with.

Taking the millipede as the original type from which
insects probably evolved—it is the millipede rather than

the centipede which actually has about 100 pairs of legs, in spite of the implications in the two names—the changes for the most part consist of reduction in the multiplicity of similar parts and partial fusion of the remainder, so that a more compact and lively product is produced. The whole remodeling process in fact could well have been a reduction in the number of legs, involving compensatory changes in the body. A millipede—note the word—driving full-speed-ahead is a fascinating sight if you are close enough to get a robin's-eye view of it, for it suggests a train moving along a track, with short legs in place of wheels, each rhythmically making a quarter-turn. It is marvelously effective, with wave after wave of successive swings of the little legs causing the long cylindrical body to glide smoothly along. That so many can be so well coordinated puts even the centipede to shame. Yet here is the point. The whole mechanism works so well because the legs *are* small, and each has to be moved but a very short distance and can be swung through its arc in the briefest of time. Longer legs operated in the same manner would get in one another's way, like typewriter key levers operated too fast when too close together. So each leg does its little bit of work in moving the body along, with the body inevitably barely clear of the ground. For greater clearance and a long stride, longer legs are necessary.

Insects have been the answer. The body has been made shorter and wider. The front end, by a process of fusion, has become a head. The long rear part, except for the tip, has become devoid of appendages altogether, and acts in part as a counterpoise to the head; only the middle section retains legs, three pairs altogether, which serve admirably for walking and standing. Three pairs of comparatively long legs, well supplied with muscles and operated from a compact mass of nerve cells in the mid-body, are far more effective than a large number of small ones, as the scuttling speed of a cockroach and the obvious success of insects on this planet indicate.

Any animals there may be that move rapidly about on the land surface of other planets must do so by means of hard movable parts operated by contractile strands of living tissue. No alternative appears to be possible. And, judging from what has happened here, the number of the levering structures which we call legs is likely to be three pairs or less. The chances are that the more advanced forms of perambulating creatures to be found elsewhere would stand foursquare or teeter on two. Simplification and centralization seem to be the rule.

One more thing about legs and such. Hard parts and soft operating tissue can stand in relation to one another in two ways. The hard levers and struts may be internal solid rods, with the muscles and tendons on the outside, as in humans and all other land-walking backboned animals; or the hard parts may form hollow cylinders, with the muscles and tendons confined within and attached to the inside of the skeletal tube, as in insects and many other creatures. Both arrangements are good, the latter especially combining strength with lightness, though with greater restriction on increase in size, which is further reason why insects and their like have remained relatively small. In any case here is another example of the limitation of possibilities. How else can a limb be made except as a jointed lever with soft and hard parts one inside the other, with only one alternative as to which is where? Are the intelligent beings of other planets big and bony like ourselves, or are they small, hollow-legged creatures with an insect-like body and perhaps an insect-like face?

Life on land is but a step into the air. True flight has been gained on four occasions during the history of the

Earth, overlooking the marginal performances of flying squirrels and flying fish. Insects, birds, and bats are with us now. The fourth aerial enterprise was that of the long-extinct pterosaurs, the flying reptiles, great and small, of the dinosaurian age though not of dinosaurian kind. Pterosaurs, birds, and bats, in that order, represent three successive and successful remodelings of the terrestrial quadruped chassis for flight in the insubstantial air. In each case the body load is lightened as far as possible, the bones especially. In each case the foreleg skeleton is transformed by processes of enlargement and reduction, into a wing-supporting structure; in each case an extensive wing surface is formed, either from skin and other tissue stretched out like a webbing as in reptile and bat, or as extensions from the skin in the form of feathers; and in all there are, or were, powerful muscles operating between breastbone and wing. Nothing has really been added or taken away, and the remodeling is essentially a restyling carried to the extreme.

In insects no remodeling of this sort has occurred. The insect wing is something new added to the original wingless insect. Two pairs of wings have evolved from the upper side of the middle part of the insect body, leaving unchanged the three pairs of legs belonging to the same part. How such wings evolved remains a mystery, for inspired guesses, however plausible, require some evidence to support them, and there is none. Yet it happened, and giant cockroaches and dragonflies already flew among the rank vegetation of the Carboniferous forests. New-fangled plastic creations or remodeled legs serve equally well as wings. What insects have done once and land vertebrates three times suggests that what has happened here could very well be accomplished somewhere else. It would be a poor world with nothing in the air.

So much for the physical machinery. What about pace and emancipation? Animals in water, except for some birds and mammals that have become marine, such as penguins, whales, and seals, have body temperatures the same as their surroundings. Any heat produced is rapidly conducted away. The range of temperature in the oceans, however, is not very great, and marine creatures can live in a fairly equable environment, cool, cold, or lukewarm, simply by not traveling too far afield. On land it is very different. Temperatures go up and down much more rapidly and to a much greater extent, which is a nuisance to all concerned. Coldblooded creatures become torpid in the heat and sluggish in the cold, and to be always in the right place, where body chemistry maintains its pace, can be a problem indeed. Independence is the goal.

So just as animals on land have become nearly independent of water, so the most advanced kinds have become independent of temperature except for extreme limits. Birds first and then mammals have succeeded in maintaining a constant body temperature as high as their body substance can tolerate without becoming like a parboiled egg. The result is that both mammals and birds operate their chemical machinery at top speed in virtually all circumstances, putting them at a tremendous advantage over all other creatures and also opening up to them territory extending from Pole to Pole. Since heat is unavoidably produced in all animal metabolism, particularly where oxygen is involved, the opportunity to conserve and exploit the production of body heat is always potentially present. There is no reason to think that this would be unique to the Earth.

Of all expectations, intelligence among the inhabitants of alien planets is presumably our greatest hope, apart from a sneaking thought that some ideally located, virginally vegetative but otherwise unoccupied planet may be wistfully waiting in the offing for mankind to colonize. All we need for the moment, however, is some assurance that minds of a sort are as likely to evolve as are the planets that might bear them. The likelihood of little minds becoming bigger minds, even to the exalted human level, we can leave to fate for the time being. Such assurance is forthcoming, at least enough to go on. Heads with a battery of sense organs, with a compact excitable brain, with associated mental activity related to awareness and action, are recognizable in three great and unrelated branches of the animal kingdom—in the octopus and its close relatives, in insects, and in vertebrates from fish to man. Granted that the higher insects and molluscs may be little more intelligent than fish, if intelligence is the word, the fact remains that the intelligent brain of apes and man was inherent in the fish, and but for chancy circumstances the molluscs and insects might have done as well. The significant thing is that the foundations for the existence and growth of intelligence have been formed in several unrelated groups of animals. Given the right encouragement, brains and minds are as likely a natural evolutionary creation as legs, hearts, or wings. In fact, machinery for travel without the navigator makes no sense. Wherever life may be, there motion will also be, and mind will follow.

E L E V E N

Is Sex Necessary?

IF SPACE SHIPS ever touch down, or at least let down, on some far and as yet unseen planet, will sex be as rampant there as here? Certainly without it the living landscape falls a little flat. That may be because we as humans are somewhat sex-obsessed, though the same could be said for almost any form of Earthly life. Sex is by no means the whole story, but it undoubtedly rules the roost. Yet before we get in too deep we should perhaps ask the leading question—is sex necessary? If it really is necessary here, then we can reasonably expect to find it in other places. If it is not really necessary, then the fuss, the furore it has created is little more than a chronic distraction to occupy our time. Actually life would be stuck without it, unable to change from the first mold into which it had been poured. Sex has become intimately associated with reproduction, yet the two are not the same. Reproduction is readily accomplished in Nature without sex entering the picture at all, though in most cases the two can no longer be disentangled. It is sex that makes the whole business both comic and desperately serious.

First, to clear the ground a little. Perhaps the most amazing quality of the living organism, apart from the sheer miracle of just being, is the capacity of a small part to grow into a new whole. Most plants and many animals, particularly the simpler, soft-bodied kinds, readily reproduce in a purely vegetative manner. Body fragments or buds can give rise to large numbers of individuals exactly like the original. Plant production from cuttings is commonplace and in nature much the same sort of thing is happening all the time. Many worms and some less familiar creatures bud off long chains of new individuals from their hinder end; some jellyfish grow new ones from around their margin and elsewhere. Given the chance to grow and multiply, almost any living cell that has not become too involved in special business may develop into the whole organism. It is a basic property of life, though it is one that is readily lost. In fact in most animals only the reproductive cells of the ovaries retain the power.

Vegetative reproduction alone, although it can produce large local populations, is a monotonous business. All individuals are alike and are spitting images of their parents. It is reproduction pure and simple, with none of the variety that is the spice of life—fine for filling up the world but no good for making change. This is where sex comes in.

If two reproductive cells from somewhat unlike parents come together and fuse, the product of development will not be exactly the same as either parent. Reproductive cells, in a sense, kill two birds with one stone. They still serve as reproductive cells whose main business is to produce new individuals essentially like the parent organism, as in vegetative reproduction; and they also introduce a little variation into the product. Rigid standardization can be a liability, for only when there is some variability can any sort of selection be made. This year's cars are

different from last year's, and one make is distinguishable
from another; even though the differences are piffling we
choose this or that and so maintain a trend.

General conservatism combined with cautious experi-
menting has resulted in the long pageant of Earthly evolution. Sex cells have been responsible, and sex cells came
long before sexes. From the start the labor has been divided among those that store up reserves but stay put, and
those that move toward them but whose matter is minimum—the eggs and the sperm. Even at the end of it all
the maid still waits for the man.

One further point before we take off. The original state
of most living things, both animal and plant, seems to have
been two sexes in one, with every individual producing
both eggs and sperm. This is still the condition in many
cases. Yet to be much good the eggs of one individual
should be fertilized by the sperm of another. This is the
problem of sex and there have been a number of ingenious
solutions among animals and plants other than the one we
are encumbered with. If creatures more or less human in
a general way have evolved on other planets, they might
just as well have had to cope with one of the alternative
situations. Suppose we take ourselves, transposed if you
like onto a more distant stage, and see how things would
have worked out if the ends of sex were just as well served
but by means other than our familiar comedy of errors. As
before, anyone can play.

The important rule to remember, to start with at least,
is that the two sexes originally belong together in one and
the same individual but that crossbreeding is necessary if
the system is not to lose much of its value. The problem is
how to arrange this. The common method is the one that
applies to humans, where the production of either the eggs
or the sperm is suppressed during the development, so that

individuals with the one or the other are females or males respectively. This situation leads to other things and also has its faults. It leaves the males, for instance, as prominently competitive for food and comfort as the females, but far less involved in the production of the next generation.

Don Juan, in Shaw's *Man and Superman,* summed up the situation this way:

"Sexually, Woman is Nature's contrivance for perpetuating its highest achievement. Sexually, Man is Woman's contrivance for fulfilling Nature's behest in the most economical way. She knows by instinct that far back in the evolutionary process she invented him, differentiated him, created him in order to produce something better than the single-sexed process can produce. Whilst he fulfils the purpose for which she made him, he is welcome to his dreams, his follies, his ideals, his heroisms, provided that the keystone of them all is the worship of woman, of motherhood, of the family, of the hearth. But how rash and dangerous it was to invent a separate creature whose sole function was her own impregnation! For mark what has happened. First, Man has multiplied on her hands until there are as many men as women; so that she has been unable to employ for her purposes more than a fraction of the immense energy she has left at his disposal by saving him the exhausting labor of gestation. This superfluous energy has gone to his brain and to his muscle. He has become too strong for her bodily, and too imaginative and mentally vigorous to be content with mere self-reproduction. He has created civilization without consulting her, taking her domestic labor for granted as the foundation of it."

Certain shrimps have done better. Each individual is both male and female but not at the same time. Each youngster grows in an ordinary way until about half full size, at which time it matures sexually and functions as a male. As it continues to grow, its maleness becomes exhausted. When it approaches full size the ovaries mature, it becomes a functional female, eggs are shed and fertilized by half-pint males, and the developing young are carried by the parent as in shrimp of all kinds. The system works beautifully. Cross-fertilization is ensured, self-fertilization is impossible, and every maturing individual contributes in the same way to the propagation of the race. It could have happened to us, and may have to the likes of us somewhere in the universe. There is no end to the implications.

Applied to humans, all halfgrown individuals, about ten years old and weighing about 75 pounds, would be males, the only males, ready to act as such both sexually and probably in other wayward ways. But as troublemakers like their truly human counterparts they would undoubtedly be kept in place by a closed society of matriarchs, roughly equal in number to the males, each twice the weight and much older and wiser. And not only wiser in a general way, but in the special sense of having each been a male herself, as understanding as a mother with a child and as little likely to put up with any nonsense, perhaps wistfully looking back to her youthful manhood. Girlhood would bud as usual when masculinity had faded, with growth continuing and full female maturity yet to come. Apart from lovelife the only question is, who would do man's work? Little men browbeaten by large women who once had been little men themselves, or the women themselves, whether fullgrown and breeding or not?

Once a basic premise is changed as in this way, there is no end to the consequences. Husbands, if such formality existed, would not only be young and small but might even not be of the same generation. Heavy broody females

would control any family life there might be. Male meno-
pause would signify more than the female, and individual
psychological adjustment to approaching male impotence
and the prospect of eventual motherhood would be eased
only by realization that such is the fate of all. Yet such a
system represents a more equitable arrangement of the
burden of living and propagating the race. It might well
have been the general pattern on Earth, with the sexes
separated in time instead of space. As it is, in most cases,
the male sex is dangerously expendable—dangerously, that
is, from the male point of view.

Theoretically, of course, we could postulate the reverse
situation, with females halfgrown and the males the larger
and older stage in the growth of the individual. Unfortunately—again for males—nature gives little support. There
are many cases within the animal kingdom of hermaphro-
dite creatures becoming first male and then female, but
none where the reverse is true. There is a developmental
reason for this, which we need not go into, and it is likely
to be as valid wherever sex has evolved as it is here. On
the other hand a regular switch from one sex to another
and back is well known among oysters and some other
rather inactive molluscs. These creatures are both sexes in
one, but male and female phases succeed one another every
few months, so that all fertilized eggs are the product of
separate parents and variable offspring are ensured. Put
this alternating turnabout into a human setting and sex
life, marital and otherwise, becomes more of a farce.

In any case the status of the female is never in doubt.
Whoever produces eggs is essential to the future, for eggs
are reproductive cells, whatever else they may be. Sperm
are not so in the primary sense of the word. They serve
two decidedly secondary ends—they serve to stimulate the
otherwise comatose eggs to start developing, like the kiss

that awakened the Sleeping Beauty, and they serve to introduce considerable variability derived from the male parent. Eggs alone are not entirely without variability, and eggs alone under certain circumstances readily develop into grown organisms, whereas sperm cannot. The mature organism is the egg developed, with usually but not always a few extra touches added by the sperm. Moreover, a very little sperm can go a long way toward meeting the needs of a breeding female population. Judging by situations all too common among the lesser fry, maleness can be the pride before the fall.

This is the basic fact all males should remember, that eggs are all that they need to be in order to develop into complete organisms. When reproduction in terms of numbers is more important than variability among the offspring, the production of a male for every female is as clear a case of featherbedding as running diesel locomotives with supernumerary engineers left over from the age of steam. One of the worst pests of the spruce forests, a sawfly, consists entirely of females whose eggs develop directly and only into more females, with never a male to be seen. The eggs develop spontaneously without need of sperm, and society is unisexual. Parthenogenesis is the rule.

Another case, with more for the mind to play on, is seen in the crustacean waterflea, sweetly known as Daphnia. Here sex and society are exquisitely in tune with the changing environment of their small worlds of ponds and lakes and puddles. Throughout spring and summer all are females busily producing only female-producing eggs— every consumer is a producer—and in no time at all a good dense population comes into being. Then overproduction and overconsumption begin to spoil their paradise, and late-season falling temperatures warn further of the shape of things to come. These are signals for a physiological switch to be pulled within each tiny body. Some eggs now form which develop into males and the population readies for the emergency. If the warnings have been false alarms, the vestal virgins go on breeding as before—parthenogenetically—and the rejected males have no propagative duties to perform. If conditions go from bad to worse, the breeding females turn another switch, produce eggs which must be fertilized, and couple with the males. Their fertilized eggs must pass through drought or frost and the return of water before they develop and renew the cycle, like seeds—long after the parental population has passed away. Males are still necessary, but only as the last resort.

It is much the same in bees, particularly the hive bee. For here the queen bee mates with a male but once, and only on her nuptial flight. Thereafter all her eggs destined to be fertilized are fertilized from sperm acquired on that occasion. Only female offspring are produced, until such time as males are needed to prepare for the nuptial flight of another queen. Somewhat later when winter is approaching, the males left over, no longer needed for the sake of sex and not otherwise doing any work, are stung to death by their busy little sisters.

Among other creatures, the successful male himself may be in jeopardy, for female scorpions, and some spiders, eat their mate when he has served his purpose, so that the otherwise wasted substance constituting the body of the male is put to good account. The praying mantis even jumps the gun and usually begins her meal while the sexual act is being consummated.

In the long run sex is undoubtedly necessary, and it would be disturbing to our concepts as well as to our feelings if none was found where life exists on other planets. Matching a male to every female, as is generally the case among Earthly things, may be merely the simplest method of making two singles out of doubles. Consequently every way you look there seems to be a superabundance of males, far more than is necessary for their purpose. In any breeding community, whether of starfish, trees, or seals, a few males can take care of a crowd of females. Polygamy may have been a significant phase in our own, prehuman, history. But nature is both prolific and profligate, and a superabundance of males means little so long as space and food are available. When excess males become a nuisance, however, they generally become reduced both in numbers and in status. Wherever social sex control has been attained, it is always for the purpose of controlling males. Motherhood is the reigning monarch.

While, therefore, it seems virtually certain that the purpose of sex must be served wherever life evolves, it does not follow that the mechanism generally but not exclusively adopted on Earth is necessarily the best. It may have been merely the most readily acquired at the time the basic choice had to be made. The alternatives we encounter here do seem to be relatively late inventions that have arisen for the sake of reproductive efficiency. Yet it is all too likely that wherever societies of any kind are of long standing and more or less fully developed, as in bee societies here, sex will be strictly under control, males will be produced only according to need, and the master race or, better, the mistress race, will not suffer their planet to be overrun by emotionally disturbed supernumerary males.

It might even happen here if human males don't watch their step. All this poking into the nature of things, whether aiming at the stars or delving into cells, is downright dangerous, for whatever we know we try to put to use. Hence the warning against eating the fruit of the tree of knowledge. Admittedly, at present we cannot practice sex control—meaning the determination of the sex of our offspring, not the control of sex in our lives, although this too is about as wild an aspect of being alive as we possess. But we do know just about all that we need to know for sex control, theoretically at least, and far more in fact than we understand about cancer. But the motive for controlling sex is not overly strong, and the funds of foundations and governments have not yet been put behind it. Sooner or later, however, sex control will be feasible and every newly married couple will want it. Then what?

The safety of the existing system is that sex, that is, maleness and femaleness, is exactly as much a matter of chance as tossing for heads or tails. The coin must come down one side or the other—or at least the number of times it rests on edge and confuses the issue is insignificant —and as long as enough tries are made the males and females among the offspring will be in balance. When every couple can decide which way it is going to be, then the boat will begin to rock. Both parents are likely to call for a male to begin with, and the die will be cast. The next generation will be heavily weighted with males, and girls will be in relatively short supply. So far, so fine for the male sex, you may say, but that is as far as it goes. The pendulum swings to make up for too many bachelors, and then the females come to the fore, and before you can turn around, a man's world changes over to a woman's world, with the mature women in full control of what proportion of males there should be. With the world taken over and males reduced in number, serving mainly for stud purposes and otherwise as a sort of pet passing from pillar to post, human society as we know it would be profoundly changed —unhappily but maybe preferably to this everlasting threat of nuclear extinction. With this near-choice already before us, there is nothing fantastic in supposing a more advanced society elsewhere may have already taken full control of its sexual constitution. Why leave it to the social insects?

Insect societies have also exploited growth control. In hive bees this concerns only the females, and concerns the division of the society into a queen and a large number of workers, leaving aside the drones. In parenthesis—drones, for all their male sexuality, are the product of unfertilized eggs; had the same eggs been fertilized, they would have produced females. But the distinction between queen and workers is a matter of growth, not sex. Bee larvae produced by fertilized eggs and fed with the hormone called the royal jelly, in addition to the regular pap, develop to the fullest extent into fertile queens. Those who don't get jelly with their bread still develop into females, but are a little stunted in their growth and stop short of reproductive maturity: sexually inhibited maids-of-all-work for the rest of their lives. To all intent a neuter sex has been created, through a rather simple developmental trick, which attends wholeheartedly to the every day business of the community, without hormonal disturbance, undistracted by importunities.

Ants and termites carry their caste system even further, and have done so independently of one another, to produce neuters of more than one size and shape. The control still lies within the ovary and, as in bees, all fertilized eggs are destined to be females and those that miss being fertilized become males. The difference is that worker bees have had their vitamin withheld during their upbringing, whereas in ants and termites there is no discrimination once the eggs have been laid, but a good deal goes on before. Eggs fully formed within the ovary eventually become queens or kings complete with wings only if they escape from the maternal body in quick time. If their exit is delayed they become partially reabsorbed, emerge reduced in size, and give rise to soldiers and workers according to the reduction they had initially undergone.

All in all, the production independently of complex, stabilized, but flexible societies in waterfleas, bees, ants, and termites by inborn manipulation of growth before and after fertilization and of fertilization itself, shows possible patterns rather readily achieved. They are not essentially different from the basic bisexual pattern in the world at large, but represent elaborations of it. These societies are of very long standing, of the order of a hundred million years, for the insect stocks in which they have appeared are old in time. Whether such a society may be the fate of man is for the future to decide. So far we just haven't been around long enough for even a trend to show. Yet on other planets possibly similar to the Earth but a little older, or on planets where evolution may have taken a somewhat similar course but a little faster, the dominant forms of animal life may well be societies of this sort. It is a possible path to survival, though heaven protect us from it here.

The late William Morton Wheeler, the most intimate human associate the ant and termite societies have ever had, once published an open letter, the Termitodoxa, ostensibly from the king of a termite society to mankind. In part it went as follows:

"Our ancient biological reformers started with the assumption that a termite society could not be a success unless it was constructed on the plan of a superorganism, and that such a superorganism must necessarily conform to the fundamental laws of the individual organism. As in the case of the individual, its success would have to depend on the adequate solution of the three basic problems of nutrition, reproduction, and protection. It was evident, moreover, that these problems could not be solved without a physiological division of labor among the individuals composing the society, and this, of course, implied the development of classes, or castes. Termite society was therefore divided into three distinct castes, according to the three fundamental organismal needs and functions, the workers being primarily nutritive, the soldiers defensive, and the royal couple reproductive. Very fortunately our earliest social ancestors had not imitated our deadly enemies, the ants, who went crazy in the early Cretaceous on the subject of parthenogenesis and developed a militant suffragette type of society, but insisted on an equal representation of both sexes in all the social activities. Our society is therefore ambisexual throughout, so that, unlike the ants, we have male as well as female soldiers and workers. It was early decided that these two castes should be forbidden to grow wings or reproduce and that the royal caste should be relieved from all labor of securing food and defending the termitarium in order to devote all its energies to reproduction. The carrying out of this scheme yielded at least two great advantages: first, the size of the population could be automatically regulated to correspond with the food supply, and second, the production of perfect offspring was greatly facilitated."

Perhaps for us the danger has already passed, and high individual intelligence makes unnecessary biologically regimented organizations as repositories for collective inherited wisdom. However this may be, here or elsewhere, sex in some form seems sure to be present.

Questions of Time

WE ARE ALL CREATURES of time. But what kind of time and how much time? We measure time by the ticking of a clock, cutting up time into seconds and matching the beat of a heart. If the heart speeds up or slows down, has time changed and is the clock in a rut? The day is divided into twenty-four hours, an hour being the time to cook a meal —twice as many hours, each half the length, would mean as much. The length of a day is high noon to high noon, the sun in the zenith. It is the turn of the Earth and, whether arbitrary or not, at least it is not a measure of a human whim. Yet Jupiter would spin out a different meter —raising the Sun at dawn five times in two Earthly days. And what are weeks but the measure of a man's work before he needs a day of rest? To measure a month requires a moon; without one or with several where would the month have gone?

And so to the years. Three-score and ten is the statistical measure of human life, though it is merely the count of the number of times the planet has moved round the sun between the coming and the going. The days in the year—

long division applied to two chancy movements, the rate of the planet's circle of the sun divided by the rate of spin about its axis, an oddment needing an extra quick step every fourth time round.

On Mars the day would be much the same as here, but there would be twice as many to make a year. On Venus the year would be one-third shorter, but seemingly without a day at all. Time here on Earth is no more than our place in the Sun—not true cosmic time and not living time at all. Elsewhere it would be different. A man living out his normal span on Venus would live about 110 Venusian years; on Mars he would count them about forty; on Jupiter six or seven. Yet his real time would not have changed.

The time of life is hard to measure when all the yard-sticks are arbitrary. It is harder yet when we realize that living time itself has a changing value. Hearts beat fast when young and slow down to a steady level only when growth is over. Even then the blood flows through veins and arteries at a slowing pace as long as life endures. And the days seem shorter as the measures of living time get longer, as though the spring of the living clock unwinds and the tension goes, until finally none is left. So all we can do, it seems, is to make comparisons.

Aesop started this in his tale of the hare and tortoise. The tortoise slowly plods his weary way and finally beats the hare who runs on a principle of fast goes and long stops. Yet had it not been for overconfidence the hare would have won before the tortoise had more than started, not so much because the hare is better constructed but because it runs at a higher temperature. The hotter the faster is the general rule, both for chemical reactions as such and for biological activities based on them.

The time allotted to any living thing may accordingly

be spent quickly or slowly according to circumstance, but in any case much faster at first than at last. Mice, for instance, live at a furious rate, with heart beating 400 times a minute and whiskers fast-quivering with excitement. How long is their day or each of their two or three years? Do they get more or less living time than the long-lived tortoise or a slow-witted sloth? However living time is measured, how long it lasts depends on both how fast the candle burns and how much candle there is to start with. Man time goes several times more slowly than mouse time, but there is much more of it altogether, much more in fact than that of any other creature.

When we reach well-inhabited planets, if ever we do, this question of time will be vitally important. Human visitors would tick away their lives as before, though perhaps losing count in terms of days or years. But the nature of any creatures that might stand or crawl or tower before us would not be fully appreciated. Shape and size and appurtenances would be seen at once, but the personal experience of alien creatures, a product of their time, would take time itself to sense or otherwise discover. A general rule, however, would be: the smaller, the shorter and faster their time. For as creatures as large as or larger than ourselves, with body warmth much the same, the common allotment here is twenty years more or less—even for the horse and whale. Apes may live almost twice as long. Only man, elephant, and parrot, among the warmblooded, draw it out to seventy years. And at that the quality of human time is unique in certain subtle ways. Individual man hopes to acquire the wisdom of his individual age, as well as that precariously passed on by his society. Yet for most of Earthly creation the individual is born equipped with the wisdom the ages—as distinct from age—already imprinted in the brain. How much of that and this are we going to find?

Time seems to be built into the very fabric of living things on Earth, and there is every reason to think that time will govern events wherever life has evolved. Whether to survive, to reproduce, to satisfy a bodily appetite or merely curiosity, it is universally important to be in the right place at the right time, and in most cases also to be in the right state of mind or body. Often enough the cues are taken directly from the regular conjunction of planetary and solar sequences. The rotation of the Earth, bringing alternating day and night to most of the Earth's surface, and the monthly rotation of the Moon around the Earth, are ready-made external clocks that serve well as time signals for the regulation of various activities of animals and plants. Many flowers close at night, bats and fireflies become active at dusk, birds wake at dawn. The fireworms of West Indian reefs come to the surface of the sea during summer months to show their ethereal living light to make a nuptial tryst, at forty minutes after sunset for the first few nights following the full Moon, when neither the Sun nor the Moon is in the sky and all is dark enough for their own small lights to show.

The surprising discovery, however, is that most living organisms have clocks built into their very being. Even a slice of raw potato has a regular 24-hour rise and fall in its rate of respiration. Certain single-cell organisms common in the sea have a 24-hour routine of growth, cell division, and production of living light, which continues day in and day out when all daily changes in light and darkness have been eliminated. They keep time with the Earth's spin in relation to the Sun without any discoverable external cues. Something in the living organism keeps time, either some component of the cell or perhaps, as in a watch, the whole thing is the clock. And not merely single cells but larger, multicellular creatures. Cockroaches, for instance, scuttle just as regularly, independent of any waning and waxing of the light. An internal rhythm, corresponding to the period of rotation of the planet, seems to be imprinted in the living protoplasm. Canceling out the rotation of Earth itself—rotating organisms on a turntable at the South Pole—once in every 24 hours in the opposite direction to the Earth's rotation, leaves the rhythms undisturbed.

Whatever the internal time-signalers may be, they have been put to good use, notably in bees and birds. In fact, the bees and the birds first made biologists aware of living clocks. Around the turn of the century August Forel, the Swiss physician and naturalist, observed that bees visiting his breakfast table each morning in search of food always arrived at the same time even when no food was offered. Half a century later it was discovered that bees could be trained to visit at any time of day, and efforts were made to discover how they could tell the time. Colonies of bees were kept in rooms with constant illumination, temperature, and humidity; daily rhythms of air ionization were eliminated with the aid of radioactive substances; cosmic radiation was eliminated by carrying out the training and testing six hundred feet below ground in the gallery of a salt mine. In all cases the punctuality of the bees remained unchanged. Finally, after World War II had come and gone, transcontinental and transoceanic air travel made it possible to train bees in one place and ship them overnight several thousand miles east or west. Bees ignored the shift and acted according to the local time they had been trained in. No doubt was left that the clock was internal and not a case of cosmic signals. Experiments with birds led to the same conclusion.

Both of these flying creatures, which keep direction in flight by keeping an angle to the Sun, are able to adjust the angle to the time of day and to the apparent shift of the Sun, so that a constant compass direction is maintained.

Rhythms within rhythms keep living organisms in tune with the Earth—rhythms incorporated in the organisms themselves so that even without guidance they keep closely in time, though the living clocks are constantly checked against solar and in many cases lunar time. The daily rhythm, however, is so ingrained and so universal among Earthly organisms that there is little doubt the 24-hour fluctuation in light resulting from the spin of the Earth entered the fabric of life at the very start. The unique value of the living clock is that it is a timekeeper *independent* of temperature change. It operates as accurately in coldblooded as in warmblooded creatures, and as well in the polar regions as in the tropics. We are creatures of time and keepers of time in the most literal sense of the word.

Wherever life may have evolved, the same necessity to keep in harmony with the twisting and turning of the planet would exist. Being on time is vital to any living thing, irrespective of whether life goes slow or fast, and the timer must derive from and relate to the planetary cycles. Where the spin is rapid the living rhythm is rapid too—how else could it be? Where there is no spin, what rhythm could there be? Only the annual period around a sun, and only then if the axis is tilted or the orbit elliptical. Possibly any planet without a spin has lost it by being too close to its sun, too close for life to evolve on, so that life without a day is non-existent.

On Earth, we as human beings are less ruled by inner clocks than is usually the case, but we still run our physiological machinery on a regular 24-hour cycle. When we fly across an ocean or a continent we continue to run on the cycle tuned to the local time of the place we left, and several days are required to reset the clock to the new time zone. Until then sleeping, eating, and such are out of kilter. Fortunately for travelers who go not only abroad but off-base, humans appear to get along fine in the long Arctic or Antarctic summers where daylight is continuous —rhythms continue with less regularity, particularly the periods of sleep and wakefulness, which tend to be alternating periods of much shorter duration. Catnapping in fact can be as satisfactory as any other pattern. It is only those creatures who can go about their business exclusively in daylight or in darkness that sleep away the whole of the other phase.

We appreciate time though we let it slip and grieve at its passing. Who else has such an awareness of time, as distinct from a timer? Possibly no other creature on Earth, and certainly none that we know of, though the ape knows enough to be bored and a monkey's curiosity knows no limits. So what possibility is there that other planets have creatures as time-conscious as ourselves, or even more so? As always the question throws back to the nature and making of man. Awareness of time depends on memory. Without conscious memory of past experience coexisting with awareness of present impressions, no awareness of the time dimension is possible. Conceivably in other creatures, particularly in the higher mammals, the immediate past survives in fairly vivid form alongside the ever-present world of the senses. Awareness of time passing and time past, to the degree that we know it ourselves, depends on a combination that is unique on Earth—a remarkably large and complex brain of a certain type and an equally remarkable amount of time for our individual lives, whether this is reckoned in living or in calendar time.

Memory is something stored, and all that you or I have ever given attention to is imprinted for total recall, from the days of our childhood until senility blurs the record. To gain access to it is another matter, though it is all there. Reflective thought is involved as well, when the record of past experience is held against the present. Time takes on reality when watching a horse race or listening to a symphony, when the whole movement of sight or sound stays in the mind from beginning to end. And as each of us grows older we hold on to our personal past in much the same way, with so much more to hold on to and so much more with which to hold it all than had our prehuman forbears. Time becomes the fourth dimension and mind begins to absorb the stars.

All of it has come about in the last moment of geological time, yet nothing suggests it could have happened any sooner. Younger planets than the Earth are unlikely to have produced time-minded creatures such as ourselves unless the pace of progress has been faster. It would be interesting, no doubt, but certainly no pleasure, to make the supreme effort of travel through space only to have a meeting of minds with a cow.

Suppose there was more time, not less, in the sense that human-like beings existed whose life span was several times as long as ours is now. George Bernard Shaw had a try at this in *Back to Methuselah*, and in the last act—"As far as thought can reach," set in the year 31,920 A.D.—he portrays a state of man where the life span is three hundred years and babes are hatched from the egg and no longer born from the womb. In a stage direction he says, "The Newly Born, a pretty girl who would have been guessed as seventeen in our day, sits up in a broken shell, exquisitely fresh and rosy, but with filaments of spare albumen clinging to her here and there." Nothing is said concerning how such a huge egg could have been produced, and we have to take it for granted as a piece of dramatic symbolism; otherwise it becomes a retrograde step from the elaborate mammalian system of live births back to the egg-laying business of reptiles and birds, from which it has been derived. Even then Shaw's huge egg would have required an egg-layer far larger than the extinct elephant bird of Madagascar which laid two-gallon eggs, the legendary Roc of the Arabian Nights. Such an egg-layer would be an interesting possibility, a sort of cross between a termite queen and a goose, and as massive as a Brontosaurus—eminently productive, but more like Mother Earth personified than anything remotely human.

All this aside, however, Shaw's account of the superhuman life cycle from conception to the grave is significant. As the midwife-priestess tells the newly hatched maiden:

> "You have been growing for two years in the egg. You began by being several sorts of creatures that no longer exist, though we have fossils of them. Then you became human; and you passed in fifteen months through a development that once cost human beings twenty years of awkward stumbling immaturity after they were born. They had to spend fifty years more in the sort of childhood you will complete in four years. And then they died of decay."

Life then continues for some hundreds of years until some accident terminates it. The living birth had been abolished; children are not even seen, let alone heard; sex is over almost at once; and creeping senescence and the sign of death never approaches—all those qualities of human life that bothered G.B.S. during his own lifetime. And speaking of man as he is, in comparison with his superman —"You must remember that these poor devils were very little better than our idiots: we should never dream of letting one of them survive the day of its birth. Why, the Newly Born there already knows by instinct many things that their greatest physicists could hardly arrive at by forty years of strenuous study. Her simple direct sense of space-time and quantity unconsciously solves problems which cost their most famous mathematicians years of prolonged and laborious calculations requiring such intense mental application that they frequently forgot to breathe when engaged in them, and almost suffocated themselves in consequence."

At the time the play was written digital computers were a generation yet to come. All the same it is just possible that the human brain is on the threshold of this sort of thing, for there have been many cases of children who could almost instantaneously make mental calculations of great magnitude, by procedures not understood, though only to lose the capacity soon after exposure to formal education. On planets older but no less productive than ours, there is not only the possibility but the probability that brains far superior to our own will have evolved. If so, and if we should ever visit such a planet and survive the alien chemistry of the place, how would we appear to beings of greater intelligence? Would we be any better than the scared and chattering monkeys we have been sending into space in flying capsules? Turn it about: if little, incoherent and seemingly scatterbrained subhumans arrived here in a flying saucer from Mars or from elsewhere, how would we treat them? Science and circuses would both make a grab for them, and after as much exhibition as they could stand they would end up in some sort of pickle jar for subsequent dissection and chemical analysis. Such, at least, is the way we treat the life already about us, unless it is the basis of blood sport or a source of food. Why should we ourselves get a better welcome on any planet already occupied by intelligent beings?

Bigger and better brains are certainly possible. One of the sorrows of an intelligent and self-conscious human is awareness of his own mental limitations—a feeling of mind imprisoned in a bony skull, supplied with restricted and censored kinds of sensory information out of which a universe has to be constructed. The limitations of supply and in the nature of the machinery are reflected in the performance.

In postulating longer lives Shaw had two points to make —that one of our troubles is that human beings do not live long enough to achieve either mental or moral maturity during the presently allotted three-score years and ten, but we might do so if we could live to the age of Methuselah, and that given the longer life span with its prospect of greater wisdom and longer perspective, such superhumans would be more considerate of the world they inhabit. Goodness knows the Earth is in sore need of respite from the attention we have been giving it for the past few thousand years. And there is little doubt that the longer the life the farther forward and backward we would look. Few people care how much the world has changed since the time of their grandfathers or how different it may be, for better or more likely worse, when their grandchildren will be grown. If personal time extended several centuries, the first children to be born of the Pilgrim Fathers—speaking broadly—might be alive now. If all else had been the same, their sense of time passing and things changing would be far more impressive and burdensome than ours.

Our individual sense of time itself changes with the passage of time. To a teenager a five-year look into the future seems like a lifetime. To a sexagenarian a fifty-year look backward seems like no time at all. We measure time subjectively, using as a yardstick what we have already experienced. From this viewpoint long-lived beings, elsewhere now or here in the future, would undoubtedly have a much more intense sense of space-time and of their own place in it than our own present emerging awareness.

Whether such an age is possible for creatures such as ourselves, on either an Earthly or Unearthly planet, depends on a number of things. The giant tortoises do pretty well as it is—at least twice our calendar time; while the red sequoias and one or two other trees live for three thousand years. Time-extended life is possible. The question is, what kind of life and what kind of time are involved?

To start with there is the matter of sheer wear and tear. Whatever it appears to be, a living thing is essentially watery stuff. A tree, to be sure, accumulates all its yesterdays in its heartwood, not too differently from the manner in which a coral reef forever grows upon the dying and dead reef skeleton. What lives is delicate stuff. It lives not by endurance but only as long as it continues to replace itself. Matter steadily flows into the living system, takes its place and then gives way to new. The flow is life. The rate of flow is the measure of life, fast at first and then slower and slower. This has already been spoken of, but now we are concerned with the utmost extension of such a system in time. How can this flow of matter which constitutes every individual creature be made to continue for a much longer time without cutting down on the rate of flow? There is no present answer, though the question will arise again.

The duration of life may depend on secondary questions. A wild horse or sheep, for instance, can crop and chew grass only as long as the teeth hold out. When they are ground down to the gums, death by starvation puts an end to life. Enamel and dentine, although alive, are so densely crystalline and so slowly replaced that what is initially formed is practically all that will be available. Increasing the life span, at least for creatures who have and must use their teeth, presents a problem. Double the years and you double the wear, that is if there is something still left to be worn. A horse can't do it. Grass is so abrasive that the exceedingly long grinding teeth wear down in less than two decades. There is no room for longer teeth, nor can teeth be made harder. Elephants. with about as much time as humans, resort to a trick. With the more or less standard equipment of four grinding molars in each side of the upper and lower jaw, they employ them in succession instead of all at once, using one immense molar at a time in line as the previous set wears out. After seventy years or so the last set has been used and the aged, hungry creature goes wild in a way even its companions cannot tolerate. Humans, with extensive and expensive aid from dentists, with a minimum of actual wear, manage to keep their teeth in useful shape for several decades, though much too commonly in the end have to substitute dentures for dentine. It is difficult to see how living longer would do more than extend the toothless aftermath—not exactly a state to look forward to. Shaw's grown-up children would have had to live on pap or its equivalent. We may come to it yet.

So enough of this, at least for the time being. Time, even living time, is more than a man's life or any other creature's. It is the sum total of time of all life on a planet from the beginning onward, and still more than that if all suns and planets are included whether life has started on them or not. The life of the Earth, in spite of its tremendous diversity, is one and a whole, and has been so since life first began. This living mantle, scintillating as this or that aspect catches the sun, has continually transformed throughout geological time. The present world and its very recent past, which is the most familiar to us, has slowly evolved to this state through an immensity of time beyond our appreciation though not beyond our facile speech. Yet even though it seems impossible to get the feeling of evolutionary time—what it means subjectively to evolve through a million years, let alone a billion—we can still map out a chart to show how long this phase of evolving life lasted compared with the next or another phase, how much time, relatively, went by before land life first appeared; what has been the pace of progress, if it can be called that, from four-finned fish to two-legged man. The time-sense here becomes a feature of the collective mind of man, the result of the concerted effort and thought of several generations of scientists. Each individual mind can now project into the past, and by extrapolation perhaps into the future, in a way and to an extent only now becoming possible.

Inevitably this leads to a comparison of the life spans of solar systems throughout our galaxy, so far as can be judged from the study of the stars whose retarded rate of spin suggests they have attendant planets. And wherever life has come into being, time as well as temperature will have played and will continue to play as great a role in its evolution as it has here. The crucial question is whether time permits as much, or more, or less emergence of sensate and mental life on planets of other solar systems, as it has on Earth. We need to look again at other suns in comparison with our own.

Singles and Doubles

EVERYTHING WE KNOW about the Earth suggests that it is a happy mean. It is neither a very small planet nor a very large one. It lies just about midway between the zones that are too hot and too cold for the support of life. It spins about its axis reasonably fast, but not so fast as some. It orbits the Sun in a year that flits by soon enough, but is not interminable nor yet too fleeting. The Sun itself is a good middle-sized star. More than this, the Sun is apparently middle-aged, with about as much time to spend before it engulfs its children as it has already spent in raising them. If anything can be a norm for life-bearing solar systems, this system and this planet should be one. Yet this is far from saying that this is the best of all possible worlds, though it may well be the best we will ever encounter.

Given a solar system to start with, what is necessary for one or more of its planets to evolve life, assuming of course that the planets themselves are qualified candidates? Above all else, a planet must revolve around its sun at a distance where it receives abundant energy and where the life-bearing medium, presumably water, can exist in liquid form—

the thermally habitable zone where heat and light are sufficient but not excessive. Such a zone varies greatly with the nature of the star. The larger the star, the greater is the overheated zone next to the star, but greater still is the zone beyond where the conditions for life are proper. The smaller the star, the narrower the hot and not-so-hot zones around it.

Look at the main sequence, already referred to, from this point of view, the main sequence being the stable state of a star that lies between its unstable infancy and its approaching death as a red giant about to explode. The sequence itself is generally shown as a curve which relates the luminosity of a star to its spectral type. The more massive the star, the brighter it is and the faster it burns. Stars are classed as B, A, F, G, K, and M, of which M is the smallest. Our Sun is a G and is the standard used for luminosity. B is more than seventeen times and A is three times as massive as the Sun. Both can be disqualified at once because they are too short-lived to support life long enough for appreciable evolution to take place. So we are left with the four types representing the middle and lower range.

Taking these in order and starting with the smallest, the M stars stay in the main sequence for about 100 billion years, but have a luminosity little more than one hundredth of the Sun; the K stars remain for about 30 billion years and have a luminosity about one fifth that of the Sun; the G stars remain steady on an average for about 10 billion years, with our Sun a G star a little above average; while the F stars, about five times as luminous as the Sun and one and one-half times as massive, endure for about 5 billion years.

Several very important features of solar systems emerge from this. First, you can't have it both ways. A long life and a merry one do not go together. Time can be too short, luminosity presumably can be too low. The planets of a small star must huddle close if they are to come to life. Conversely, the larger the star the more room there is for such planets to play in. But questions come at once. Do small stars have small planets and do their planets move in orbits closer to their sun, or are a small star's planets more likely to swing in the cold beyond the pale? At present we can only guess.

And what about stars that have companion stars big enough to interfere with the perfect or nearly perfect circularity of their small satellite orbits? Since about half of the stars in our neighborhood are binary and multiple systems and this proportion is probably typical of the galaxy as a whole, does plurality favor the presence of life, or not? The answer is clear enough. Plurality is of no help, and is most likely to be harmful.

If the two stars of a double star system are relatively far apart, as many of them are, a planet which circles around and between them both might conceivably enter the life-supporting zone of each for a while, but would also for a comparable length of time be traveling in the interstellar regions outside these zones. It would be as if the Earth circled half way round the Sun and then took a figure-eight course way out beyond Jupiter for a shorter period around another sun. Life could not survive the trip, nor could it ever have got started. So also with planets in single orbits around double stars that are close together, even if one star should be very much smaller than the other, as is often the case. The life-bearing zone although no longer circular would still be nearly so, but the planet's orbit would be more strikingly elliptical and most probably would take the planet too far away from its double sun for a considerable part of its orbit—enough to hinder the start of life and probably enough to prevent it.

Without looking for anything other than liquid water as the medium and basis for life, this range of stars and the possible variety of planets located within the life zone, when taken as a whole, offers unlimited possibility of variation in planetary surface conditions. It is hardly more likely that a life-supporting planet would be exactly duplicated than it is that a particular man will be duplicated on the Earth unless he happens to be one of identical twins, in which case there was only one egg to start with and it is cheating of a sort.

Star-oriented scientists who have discussed the possibility of planets associated with the Milky Way stars, particularly in connection with the smaller stars of the slow-burning categories, have suggested that while such stars are far more numerous than stars like the Sun or larger, they have such a narrow life-supporting temperature zone that the chance of a planet being in such a zone is relatively small. This raises an unresolved problem of the origination of a solar system as such. We have only our own to study at first-hand, and the events we are concerned with lie five billion years in the past. That is a long time ago, and the best we can do is to construct models that will more or less account for things as they are. The one that accounts for the most of the present peculiarities, that introduces no incongruities, and makes the fewest initial assumptions, will be the most widely accepted, to be displaced only by one that might say—anything you can do I can do better!

According to the model currently in favor, a solar system such as ours begins as a slowly rotating and contracting dust cloud. As the cloud contracts and the spin increases, the mass first becomes spherical and then begins to flatten out along its spinning axis, just as the Earth's spin causes it to flatten slightly at the Poles and bulge a little at the equator. When the original dust cloud has contracted to less than one thousandth of its original size and its rotation is relatively rapid, a disk grows out of the equatorial matter, spinning out farther and farther, with the lightest material extending the farthest. The central material becomes the sun, slowly becoming hot and shining as its diameter grows smaller and its density increases; while the warm, outwardly moving disk of dust eddies successively as it goes. Condensation proceeds as the distance from the center increases and the temperature drops—the iron and silicates with their high boiling points liquefying first; then water, ammonia, and other gases liquefy and freeze; while most of the hydrogen, predominant to start with, escapes from the system altogether.

The planets arise from the eddies or turbulence within the dusty disk. The eddies increase in size in a general way from the inner to the outer edge of the disk, and this, partly at least, accounts for the great differences in size of the planets and their mathematical spacing from the sun. After all, Kepler found the rule for spacing and left room for the undiscovered asteroids in an empty orbit between Jupiter and Mars. There *is* a rule for spacing, and there is almost certainly one for size. In all probability the pattern of one solar system is similar to another's, though differing in scale. That is, a small dust cloud gives rise to a small sun with a correspondingly small disk out of which form relatively small planets relatively close together. If such should be the case, the small, long-lived M and K stars are as likely to have one or two planets within the life zone as are larger stars, but the planets themselves are likely to be proportionately small. The question would then be, how small could a planet be and still possess mantles of water, crust, and atmosphere in which life could originate and evolve?

If the planets were no more massive than the Moon the answer is depressingly clear: with or without a spin and a magnetic core, the outer envelopes of gas and water would slowly but inevitably escape into space before significant life could arise, leaving merely a sterile corpse of a planet behind. It seems like a pitifully wasted cosmic experiment, when systems of this sort can endure in stable form for ten or more times as long as the one we inhabit. Wishful thinking would look at least for Earth-sized planets in the small-sun systems, even though the chance of being located within the zone for life may be decidedly small.

One of Nature's most striking characteristics, however, is her apparent willingness to waste a lot in order to create a little—a sculptor with mountains of trash at the base of the god. Perhaps we are too much impressed by too much time. Perhaps it is far from a pity that overabundant M stars, outnumbering stars like ours by ten to one, may fail to support life. Their planets at the best might be little old runts fostering a stunted growth no better than Mars' but drawn out through near-eternity.

At the other end of the scale are, presumably, planet-bearing stars much greater than the Sun but of much shorter life. Their life zone would be wide and most likely their planets large in keeping with the whole, with again one or two properly placed. All that has been said concerning the nature of life on a large, massive planet would apply. The critical question is, how long could the act last? Which raises one of the most fundamental problems concerning the study of life: what determines the rate of evolution?

The general opinion concerning the mechanism for evolutionary change is that environmental requirements select among innumerable small variations exhibited by successive generations of any particular species of organism. If the species is perfectly suited in every way to its surroundings, the members of a new generation most resembling the parental generation will be the most likely to survive and reproduce in turn, and those that vary from this standard the most will have more difficulty and may not contribute at all to a new generation. Natural Selection can in this way maintain the status quo. On the other hand if the adjustment of organism to environment is not perfect, for any reason such as a change in the environment itself or a shift of the organism to a new region, the individuals of a new generation which are most like the parental norm will be less suited to the new circumstances; other, more deviating individuals are likely to be better suited and will consequently leave more of their own progeny to perpetuate the race. Natural Selection, so-called, here favors a new trend, that is to say, evolution.

The immediate question is, how fast do such trends progress? Clearly the environmental pressures and the extent or range of variation within the species both are involved. Variation itself results from two procedures. The hereditary material in the reproductive cells of virtually every living thing consists of an enormous number of genes. Where sexual reproduction is the rule, no two reproductive cells will have exactly the same genic constitution, and each new individual produced will be a little different from all others as the result of some reshuffling in the sets of genes acquired from its two parents. This is called biparental reassortment, and it is the basis of the great variety we see, for instance, among any particular human race, and it is variation of this sort, produced in this way, that natural selection mainly works upon.

At the same time, however, changes known as mutations occur frequently in the gene substance, produced by some chemicals and by the more shattering kinds of cosmic radiation including ultraviolet light, X-rays and radioactive particles. The great majority of such mutations are harmful, lessening the chances of self-propagation of their owners. Those that are tolerated, however, become a part of the hereditary reserve, or gene pool, of the race, and in the course of time an enormous stock of potential variables piles up. In humans this stock is so enormous that the possible reassortment is practically infinite without the addition of any new mutations.

Such is the background for looking at the rate at which evolutionary changes may take place. Exposure to greater radiation than that to which life on Earth is accustomed would increase the rate at which new mutations would occur. If the hereditary material of organisms on other planets is essentially similar to what it is here, greater exposure to solar radiation, whether because of being closer to a sun or from having a less protective atmosphere, would also produce mutations at a greater pace. This alone is unlikely to affect the rate of evolutionary change, except perhaps during the very early stages in the evolution of life when gene reserves are none too large. Conceivably a very high mutation rate could be a liability, since so much that is harmful would continually have to be weeded out. This is a human prospect if we let atomic radiation of our own making get out of hand, whether from nuclear war or, more likely, improper disposal of waste from atomic energy production.

The whole problem is full of puzzles. If the rate of mutation is not the answer, what about the rate of biparental reassortment which occurs with each new generation? If this is responsible, then the shorter and more frequent the generations the more the reshuffling goes on and the faster the evolutionary process should be. Mice, which pack forty generations into the lifetime of an elephant, should have evolved relatively rapidly. Yet elephants have evolved at least as fast as mice.

Then there is the record of life itself. During the last two hundred million years certain lizard-like reptiles not only gave rise to the great diversity of the dinosaurs, but also by more profound transformation to the birds and mammals. To put it briefly, some reptiles eventually became transformed into men, but other reptiles changed not at all and still possess the ancient third eye in the top of their head that all at one time possessed. There are living fossils everywhere—not only primitive reptiles but lung-breathing fish in the swamps of three continents, and elaborate antiques such as the horseshoe crab, all virtually unchanged since time out of mind. A changing or a new environment apparently puts the pressure on, offering all life a triple choice: to evolve into new forms equipped to meet new circumstances; to retreat to such small regions where the old circumstances still prevail, there to persist unchanged; or to give up and become extinct. For most the choice has been between the first and last.

If the average temperature of a planet were hotter or cooler than on Earth at present, would evolution be correspondingly fast or slow? Again we get a dusty answer. In the first place the Earth itself throughout most of the past half-billion years has been decidedly warmer than at present and has seen great evolutionary spurts and also less creative periods. Moreover, when one group of animals or plants has been making strides, another has stood as pat as can be. On the other hand evolutionary change appears to have progressed as rapidly as anywhere and at any time here during the recent Ice Age, a cold period for much of the world, lasting for less than a million years. Heat or cold appears to make little difference, and all that matters seems to be the stress and opportunities imposed or offered by the environment, and the capacity of the hereditary gene reserve to produce varieties able to adjust or take advantage. So the question remains. We cannot tell, on the basis of our present imperfect understanding of the evolutionary mechanism as it occurs on Earth, whether in the different circumstances that would prevail on another planet the evolutionary process could be any faster or more productive than it is here. Conditions could cramp its style, undoubtedly, as they can almost any activity and not the least the biparental sort. The factor of importance above all else is that of time. Given time enough any process, no matter how slow, will reach its end.

The total time assigned to the Sun during its life as a well behaved resident of the main sequence is more than ten billion years, of which less than half has already been spent. Obviously the story of the living Earth is far from over, whether or not man in the form of whatever his descendants might be will be around. Life has probably been evolving on Earth for at least three billion years and possibly more, though for the most part it has been in a comparatively intangible form. The evolutionary transformation of a more or less primitive aquatic life into the present terrestrial world of flowers, insects, birds, beasts, and humans has been an event of no more than the last several hundred million years, with human intelligence in its present state for some hundred thousand years at the most.

From this we can draw two conclusions. Given much the same circumstances and no faster a rate of evolution, several thousand million years are required for a planet to evolve intelligent life comparable to our present achievement. And, as human beings, we have in a sense opened our eyes to the universe only in the last second or so of Earthly time—it is not strange that we understand so little of the scheme of things, it is remarkable that we seem to understand so much after our first few blinking moments of true wakefulness.

Putting the question therefore to other suns and their planets we probably must draw the line at the F stars, one and one-half times as massive as our Sun but with a total life expectancy of about four or five billion years. Given a faster break, such systems might produce intelligent life comparable to our own, perhaps even some hundreds of million years sooner if the inconceivably slow earliest phases of evolving life could be accelerated. Even so theirs would be a tragic outlook, like an old man's after a very full lifetime but with no grandchildren to represent the future. Even for stars midway between F and G, only one-third as massive again as our Sun, the entire life expectancy is still a mere six billion years—a good chunk of time admittedly, but with far more time given to the *creation* of intelligence, assuming that to be in the cards, than for intelligence and whatever else there may be to flower to the fullest. The select among the stars therefore appear to be those single stars in the bracket G to K, with life expectancies ranging from twelve to thirty billion years; with mass ranging from a little greater than the Sun down to about two-thirds of it; and with brightness from about twice as great as the Sun's to about one-fifth. A well placed planet of any of these would have no cause for complaint, as long as there was no solar competition for its allegiance. Planets, like people, cannot obey two masters, at least with any satisfaction to themselves.

Although double star systems are less likely than singles to be favorable to life, they are not entirely to be ignored and in any case they have a special interest with regard to the detection of remote and unseen planets. The fact is that only in the case of double or triple stars are we at all likely to detect the presence of nearby planets.

In the case of two stars very close together, one star moves about the other in an orbit, like a planet around its sun except that each moves around the other and each has a relative orbit that is an ellipse. But if one of the stars has a planet, the ellipse is no longer perfect, but is an ellipse with a small oscillation introduced. From the size of the oscillation the mass of the invisible third body can be estimated. The necessary observations have to be very delicate, for the disturbance created by a planet ten times the mass of Jupiter would, seen from the Earth, be no greater than the width of a pinhead seen from a distance of about seven miles.

Only the largest planets are therefore likely to be detected, and while such planets so much greater than Jupiter are heavy by our own solar-system standards, they are much too small for a star. A number of them are now known. Recently, however, a planet-sized dark companion has been detected by the same means revolving around a dim star some six light years distant from the Sun. This must be truly a planet, for it is only half as big again as Jupiter and it is associated with a single star, the star being about one seventh the mass of the Sun and the planet about one hundredth the mass of its star. This means that the star has a mass only half that of a typical M star, almost as small as a star can be and still fit on to the main sequence, and its planet is, like those detected about the double stars, remarkably large in proportion. Yet if the parent star had been greater, the small planet would not have caused enough disturbance to have been discovered. So our wishful thought that small stars might have planets large enough for life receives some highly significant support.

Life on a planet moving about one star in a double star system would seem very strange, supposing existence to be possible, even if the planet rotated on its axis in a fairly rapid and regular manner. When the planet was on the far side of its own star from the companion star, normal day and night would occur. This would be during only half the year. During the other half-year the second star would be where the night sky should have been, and as one sun set the other would rise—half a year of daily rhythm and half a year of continuous light.

Temperatures also would necessarily vary greatly according to such circumstances, not only because of the alternating semi-annual exposure to one sun and two, but because of the elliptical nature of a planet's orbit. If the temperature was suitable for life during part of the annual cycle, it could not be for all of the time. If it was right when the distance from one or other or both stars was greatest, then it would be far too hot for life when at its closest. No life could evolve under such conditions. On the other hand, if the temperature was fitting when the distance was shortest, it would be far too cold for active life when the distance was longest. This is a different situation, for it is conceivable that alternating phases of congenial warmth and cold storage might permit life to originate and evolve, though always with the need to suspend the processes of life during the periods of cold. Such suspension would be the most dominating single circumstance affecting life as a whole.

Living organisms can tolerate submission to temperatures far below the freezing point of water, but only if they pass through the freezing point so rapidly that ice crystals have no time to form within the living substance, for ice formation destroys it. This would rule out forms of life that need to maintain any sort of circulating fluid, and therefore most forms of life like those familiar to us. Nor is it likely that the seasonal change from warmth to extreme cold could be other than gradually fatal for watery organisms. Only if they underwent complete dessication could they survive the transit, and while this requirement does not exclude all possible forms of life, it would almost certainly restrict them to simple sorts such as slime molds and such. Planets of binary systems would undoubtedly be interesting enough in their way, but would be no place for the like of us or probably even for a worm. Why double star systems should be so common throughout the galaxy is another problem, possibly of great significance in the scheme of things, but far from being understood.

In the end we are left with the range of single, middle-class stars of the main sequence, not much greater nor very much smaller than our Sun. These are the stars most likely to have well regulated solar systems where life-supporting planets are to be found, and it is on their planets that our galactic compatriots are most likely to be. If we are ever to communicate with anyone but ourselves, it is there we will find them. If so, then in what state shall we find them? If all the solar systems got off to a good start at the same time, which is conceivably just possible if the big bang theory of the beginning of the universe is valid, then we might be as advanced as any. Yet even so it is probable that within every well established galaxy, stars and solar systems are continually coming into being, and systems of the same sort as ours may be much younger or much older, as well as many about the same. Supposing events to have taken much the same course as on Earth, an easier supposition to picture than anything more strange, then some living planets might still be in the early soupy stage, others somewhat fishy, others again launching the fowls of the air, and some, perhaps a billion or more years ahead of where we stand now. In any case we had better watch our step.

F O U R T E E N

Talking to the Natives

MEETING THE FOLK who live on another planet under the light of another sun, not knowing beforehand whether they will seem like morons or whether they will think we are, and not knowing whether they will be repulsive or merely strange to look at, will be accompanied by a certain amount of trepidation—far more, if we have any sense of what we are doing, than if trespassing within the sanctum of a cageless zoo. Supposing intelligence to be awaiting, who or what will we try to talk to and how would we go about it? Russians are said to be encouraging their potential astronauts to develop mental telepathy among themselves, an obviously useful approach to exobiological communication if successful, but a disturbingly indigestible matter for neurophysiologists if finally shown to be a fact.

This raises the whole issue of how to get along with natives of any place, and how to communicate with them, when they look different, have different ways, and speak a different language. There is no need to leave the Earth to find any of the problems involved in the meeting of strangers, except for the possible encounter with intelli-

gence far superior to our own. Whether we need to leave
the Earth to find greater wisdom is another matter. In any
case, before we take off for space beyond time, we should
study more closely the nature of communication itself and
we should also endeavor to communicate with some of the
lesser folk of our own planet. If we cannot get in touch,
with some degree of intimacy, with a porpoise, for instance,
which is an intelligent mammal with a brain as big as a
man's, what prospect is there that we could do so with anyone more alien to ourselves? Even if we have to talk down
to our fellow inhabitants, the exercise not only would be a
very valuable sort of training but should be a salutary experience. For it is high time man discovered who he is in
this world and that there are other kinds of minds and
other kinds of mental universes, however restricted, besides our own. The challenge which awaits us if ever we
land on another inhabited planet and wish to get to know,
if not necessarily to be known, awaits us here. Even without communication, how else are we going to appreciate
what may be found unless we can in a way put ourselves
inside the other creatures? As Hokusai, the Japanese artist,
said—"to paint a bird, you must be a bird."

Before we get too deep into this business of getting to
know the relatives, it may be best to see who communicates
with whom, to what effect, and by what means. To start
with, what goes on below the surface of the sea? If we exclude porpoises and whales because they are still air-breathing mammals that have returned to the sea, communication is at a minimum. Jacques Cousteau went so far as to
give his book the title *The Silent World,* and a silent world
it is, in spite of the illusion of considerable sound when
heard over highly-amplifying listening instruments. Sound
plays no significant role, while even light is subdued—fish
and squid move in schools, each individual keeping its

neighbors in sight of the corners of its eyes, but little more; some fish, particularly in fresh water, have courting procedures involving sight and touch. Smell and touch, each a possible basis for communication, are mainly employed for a one-way communication with prey or predator. To find anything like the real thing, again excluding porpoises and such, we have to climb out of the water, not so much onto the land as into the air.

Sound and light pass much more freely through the compressible and relatively transparent air. Hearing is primarily a sense acquired in relation to air, and even in the sea and other waters the animals in possession of this sense, the bony fish, porpoise, and others, have at some time had association with air; the more consistently submarine squid and octopus on the other hand appear to be as deaf as a post. And vision, although primarily evolved under water, is much enhanced when on the land where light is much less absorbed. Even smell seems to take on a new dimension.

Communication demands a two-way process. Something must be sent if it is to be received, although this is not the beginning. The senses of smell, sight, and hearing serve generally as warning systems for the individual in relation to the outside world, and only in a comparatively few kinds of animals are they a basis for communicating with other members of their own species. Where they do so serve, they are associated with some sort of broadcasting mechanism. And, as might be expected, this has evolved in the two dominant groups of terrestrial animals—the insects and vertebrates.

Insects employ both sight and sound, as well as smell, and in the simpler cases exclusively for a meeting of the sexes. A female night-flying moth rests on a tussock or some other suitable site and emits a musky odor into the night air.

Males downwind as much as a mile fly through the darkness directly toward her, keeping direction by means of their two widespread antennae where the sense of smell is located. Other insects sing for their mates, by rubbing hind legs together (as in locusts and grasshoppers) or by a sort of ratchet device on the abdomen (in cicadas). No matter who hears the noise, the seductive quality is felt only by the opposite sex of the species concerned, which presupposes a receiving apparatus. Insect ears, consisting of eardrum, with air chamber on the inside as well as air outside, a necessary condition for the drum to vibrate to airborne sound waves, and sense cells for response to the vibration, are located anywhere but in the head—on either side of the body below and behind the wings, or in the shank of the foreleg. In some, as in the mosquito, the humming vibration made by the wings of the female is picked up by the male through his antennae.

Frogs are little better. Their eardrums, like ours but flush with the surface of the head, lie between an outer and inner air space and conduct to vibration-sensitive cells. But, although sensitive to a wide range of sound, the total equipment of drum, sensory structure, and brain responds mainly to the sex call of another frog and to the ominous sound made by the splash of frog jumping into water.

All this is communication at its lowest but most vital level. It is carried to its perfection in the firefly, where light and sight take the place of sound and hearing. The insect eye is the natural receiver, but the female insect brain is attuned to a flashing light of a certain rhythm— a particular rhythm for a particular species. The male not only has a light-producing physiological mechanism on his abdomen, but has the capacity to flash at one and only one meter. With the female giving off light signals from the top of a blade of grass, as from the control tower of an airfield, and the male flashing his direction-calling signals as he comes in for a landing, the sexes come together and all is well.

Elaborate communication of an awe-inspiring kind goes on in the society of bees, and this in spite of the fact that the small bee brain has but one ten-millionth of the number of brain cells present in the supposedly superior human brain. Admittedly, our brains are truly superior, but in certain ways a bee can outperform them. First, what is it that social bees need to communicate? Their chief activity outside the hive is the gathering of honey and pollen, and community efficiency depends on communal effort. The more effectively scout bees communicate information concerning the location of a productive flower pasture, the better. There is no need to go into the whole fascinating story, and only the essentials of the more complex type of performance is given here.

When a foraging bee a mile or so from its hive discovers a source of perfumed sweetness, it carries back to the hive not only the actual qualities of smell and taste of the food obtained, but also the distance and compass direction of the source. In a manner unknown to us it retains some sort of record of its compass direction, taken from the position of the sun but allowing for the time of day, and it also has a record of sorts of the distance it has flown to get home. If it lands on a horizontal platform outside the hive entrance, it performs the so-called waggle dance, a reversing circular dance with a straight run along the circle's diameter, with the abdomen wagging as it goes. The direction of the straight run is the compass direction to the food, and the number of runs is an indication of distance, the smaller the number the greater the distance. All this is ingrained, for a certain number of runs performed by bees of one species indicates a different distance from that understood by bees of another species, and interbreeding two species differing in this manner results in a progeny confused.

Dancing in the light on a flat surface, however, is performed naturally only by some primitive species of honeybee, and the real performance of the more advanced bees takes place in the darkness of the hive on the vertical surface of a comb. The same information is conveyed, but now the vertical plumb line of gravity serves as the line to the sun and the direction of the straight run in the dance diverges from this to the same extent as the compass direction to the food. With so minute a computer, how can all this be accomplished?

On the receiving end, the hive bees cluster around the dancer, apparently excited by the vigor of the dance, and one by one they catch the rhythm. Human investigators have even succeeded in talking to them in their own language, by introducing a scented artificial bee on the end of a wire and causing it to wag and move in a particular direction. By this means bees have been successfully instructed to go out for food of a certain kind located at a certain distance in a particular direction. Bee communication, however, goes even further, for in follow-up experiments it was noted that at the end of an imitation dance, the watching bees often rushed in to sting the dancer, and that it was necessary for the dancer to keep on dancing until one or more watchers emitted a small "beep," apparently meaning "message understood," though by what means it is produced and heard is completely unknown. Yet there is a world here of smell, rhythm, space, and even a little sound, that we are rather successfully entering into, at least to the extent that we realize it exists and that it is far different from the world of our own senses. The challenging question is, how can so much be accomplished with so little? The possibility that on planets elsewhere in the

universe much greater mental performance than the bee's
—what else can we call it?—may be accomplished by brains
still very much smaller than our own cannot be ignored.
After all, an infant monkey ten inches high, with a plum-
sized head, shows about as much awareness and intelligent
understanding as a giant, prehuman ape.

Before we look more closely at creatures more of our
own kind, a brief glance at the inner world of the octopus
may be illuminating. The octopus has so much to work
with, and yet seems to have fallen just short of following
through to higher things. Communication with other octopi, apart from mating get-togethers and also possibly
scaring off intruders by going through a rapid series of
skin-color changes, is probably non-existent. But the animal has a good brain, as such brains go, with large sensory
lobes, a central coordinating mass, and an impressively
large part which has been identified as the storehouse of
memory. It can readily learn from experience, as experiments have shown, and it shows every evidence of being
emotional—apparently flushing with anger or impatience
when circumstances provoke it, and often going white
when under attack, as though in fear. And all the senses,
except that of hearing, are there, particularly sight and
touch, with balance and chemical senses better developed
than in most others of its kind. Hearing would be senseless
in that silent world. Within its world, therefore, the octopus is about as aware as it is possible to be, with a battery
of diverse sense organs continually firing into the central-
ized nervous system we call a brain. There is intelligence
of a sort, and it is study of octopus intelligence that has
given the clue to the circumstances under which intelligence arises.

The basic requirement appears to be the presence of
several kinds of major sense organs relating the animal to

the outside world. The larger these are, relative to the size of the animal, the better. With such an array, the sensory nerves from the sense organs will continually transmit rapid-fire stimuli into the central receiving and coordinating brain. The more incessant the firing and the more numerous the incoming channels, the greater the general level of brain excitation. This is the situation in the octopus.

An alert consciousness depends upon intense and incessant sensory stimulation. When the input ceases, as in the dark silence of the night, the level drops and sleep ensues. In the case of humans and other mammals, the brain has become relatively so massive that apparently a booster is necessary. This is the so-called alarm system in the brain stem, which, in the wakeful brain, continuously fires to the cortex and elsewhere. During sleep it lies like a watchdog, dozing perhaps but ready to arouse the household—any unusual stimulus reaching the sense organs, such as the cry of a baby or the smell of smoke, sets off the alarm system which then awakens the rest. Anything that permanently damages this arousal region in the brain stem, as too often happens in car accidents and occasionally from a slight slip of a brain surgeon's knife, causes permanent coma. Permanent, that is, until the unconscious brain and body can no longer be kept alive.

The internal world is a filtered, censored, and imperfect representation of the world outside, and each private, personal world necessarily reflects the scope and limitations of the particular set of senses the owner possesses. And not only the kinds of senses, but their relative importance and the extent to which they may be associated with one another.

To take the octopus again: it has an extremely extensive and well developed sense of touch particularly associated with the end of its eight long arms and their numerous suckers. Much of the brain is concerned with receiving the messages from this body surface. It also has a pair of very large and extraordinarily well constructed eyes, each with a relatively enormous optic lobe for the integration and recording of visual impressions. The creature's world is clearly mostly of things seen and felt. But this inner world of sight and touch has two limitations—sight and touch are not at all well brought together in the brain, compared with the eye-hand collaboration in men and apes, and the octopus fails to employ its equipment to anything like its full potential; the other is that it can make sense of what it sees only as long as its eyes are held level, for its retinal cells are arranged on a grid-like pattern and give correct information only if the organs of balance keep the axis between the eyes on a horizontal plane; a cockeyed octopus cannot properly orient itself in space even though its space be liquid.

And so with other creatures. Honeybees, for instance, are blind to red but can see ultraviolet light which we cannot. Cats quiver with ecstasy at the smell of decayed fish, but are cold to the smell of flowers. The whole group of mammals in fact, with some very notable exceptions, lives mainly nose-to-the ground in a world of smells incorporated in a monochromatic landscape. Humans, in keeping with apes and monkeys among the mammals and with all the birds of the air, have a private many-colored but odorless world. The dog's world is almost all odor and no color, as G. K. Chesterton expressed it so vividly:

> The brilliant smell of water,
> The brave smell of a stone,
> The smell of dew and thunder,
> The old bones buried under.

In the spirit of Hokusai, as an effort to get inside the skin of another creature, a maser-optics physicist, Jerome Rothstein, has gone to an extreme:

"The suspicion remains, however, that intelligent beings very differently endowed than we are might come up with a very different picture of the world. . . . In an effort to see how reasonable the possibility that we are all being fooled really is, we shall try to sketch how science might develop for a race of blind, deaf, highly intelligent worms living in black, cold, sea-bottom muck, and possessing only senses of touch, temperature, and a kind of taste (i.e., a chemical sense). These hypothetical creatures are chosen because they seem to be about as different from human beings as they possibly can be and still be able to learn things about their environment. They have no eyes, ears, or hands. They cannot use the sun or the stars to give them notions of time. They do not have natural rulers a 'foot' in length because they have no feet, and indeed, their shape is very elastic. As a rule of the game, we impose the condition that only the concepts they can use are those that develop by intelligent and imaginative thinking about the experience available to them.

"We assume that they communicate with each other, pass information from one generation to another, and that information storage is not limited by the memories of any finite number of wiggleworms. Their language need not be phonetic—it might be tactile, chemical, or even electrochemical. . . . The communication channels will, of course, utilize sensory channels, and in particular, those channels by which information is obtained about the world. This may well be what makes language possible in the first place, for words are, to a large extent, encapsulations of experience. They have semantic content in mediating communication between individuals to the extent they draw on common experience. One might even argue that the world exists objectively because we can talk about and concur in our descriptions of aspects of it! The development of language thus appears to be essentially the first phase of the development of science either for Wiggy or for us.

"Wiggy will sooner or later discover pebbles, bones, shells or similar objects in the muck. Manipulating a pebble is an experience that can be shared by many wiggleworms, so primitive concepts of rigidity and ooziness can soon become public. We assume that gravitation operates in Wiggy's world; even if he is neutrally buoyant in his oozy medium, he can discover that it is easier to move a pebble to one side than to raise it, or that a raised pebble settles back in place. He can thus generate primitive concepts of force and work, which can be encapsulated in the public language. From pebbles he can develop the concept of a rigid body and convert his topological space into a metric space. . . . Many chemical reactions produce gases. Sooner or later Wiggy may find a gas bubble trapped under a shell. He will then realize there is more to his physical universe than wiggleworms, enemies, food, ooze, water and hard objects. He will learn that these bubbles have paradoxical properties; they fly up instead of falling down. Eventually some bold wiggleworm 'astronaut' may emerge into the water from the safety of the ooze, his 'spaceship' a shell using a gas bubble to attain close to neutral buoyancy."

The ultimate challenge to our ability to understand the inner world and an actual language of another creature is the porpoise, though the human caricatures presented by various apes and monkeys should also give us pause. Porpoises are suckling mammals that live in the shape of a fish. Fortunately for them, considering our lethal attitude toward most of our Earthly companions, they are too small to have much commercial value individually, unlike the giant whales, and are too agile to be readily caught. As joyful inhabitants of the oceans they may survive our human adolescence.

Here is Cousteau again:

"One watches them race the bow of a ship, vaulting out of the foam for breath and dropping out of the stream like a man falling from flight, to be replaced instantly by another porpoise; and, as the bow speeds, lie on their flanks and spy the humans with quick little eyes. A mother swims with her child, which moves at a faster rhythm to keep up; they jostle each other playfully. Presto, for no apparent reason, the ranks thin out—the last porpoise sounds and a curtain of foam is drawn out over the ballet of the sea. We often watched and occasionally dived with them. They played chasing games as if they had a brain capacity for satire. They are constructed disturbingly like men. They are warmblooded and breathe air and are the size and weight of men . . . lungs like ours and a brain as big as a man's, deeply corrugated in the fashion that is supposed to mark human genius. Porpoises have smiling lips and shining eyes. They are gregarious and, more than that, social. There are probably more porpoises in the sea than there are men on earth. The powerful horizontal flukes of the porpoises speed them to the surface to take an instant breath, then they dive like a living torpedo. . . . Swimming under water among them with naked ears we heard their mouselike squeaks, a comical cry for such splendid animals. . . . They were running true for the Straits (of Gibraltar). Wherever they came from the porpoises had secure knowledge of where the ten-mile gate lay in the immense sea. Are the porpoises equipped with sonic or ultrasound apparatus by which their squeaks give them the feel of unseen bottom topography?"

The more one considers the porpoise, the more fascinating it becomes. In terms of biological engineering and as an example of transforming old models into new, it is as outstanding as any. Especially since porpoise language may be the most advanced among nonhuman creatures. The transformation of a fish to a four-legged land-walking animal was a major piece of redesigning. Reconverting the quadruped to the design of a fish but with the power plant of a mammal under the hood is just as remarkable a performance. This must have happened when mammals as such were fairly fresh on Earth, for the whale-porpoise type was already well established in the seas sixty million years ago, as were the equally mammalian bats flying in the air. The road to man was taken much more hesitantly and belatedly.

Before we get involved in porpoise sound effects and our efforts to comprehend their significance, the whole porpoise deserves some attention. To begin with, the original odd-shaped perambulating, whisk-tailed body of the mammal has been streamlined for passage through resistant water more efficiently than in any fish or man-made vessel, mainly by eliminating almost all trace of the hind limbs. covering the body with fat and molding it into shape, adding horizontal flukes to the tail, and converting forelimbs to lateral fins. A porpoise can stay under water for six minutes without coming up for air, and lives most of its 30-year life span in continual motion—dozing only in snatches, partially submerged with closed eyes, for rarely longer than half a minute. The young are born alive, and munch on small squid when six months old but continue to suckle for a year and a half. Vision is good, but restricted by the optical properties of sea water. Hearing is extraordinarily sensitive, as it is in bats, and is associated, as also in bats, with the use of voice in echo-location, or sonar. And again, as in some but not all bats, the creature sings or speaks through its nose, for mouths are meant for feeding and are better closed when not, particularly when speeding under water. The continually wagging of our own jaws and exposure of our tonsils is something we have to put up with in order to communicate. There are neater ways of doing it.

The porpoise nose, if we can call it that, is a single crescent-shaped nostril, or blowhole, on the top of the head, that closes upon contact with water. This is the source of the voice, for the porpoise can vibrate it in much the same manner as the human lip, and the voice can be used to send out a continual clicking sound for echo-locating the solid objects in the sea around it, or for chattering to its companions, or even to mimic a human voice and laughter if given a model to mimic. Add to all this a genuine sense of fun and an amazing ability in aquatic acrobratics, and the porpoise becomes a fellow creature indeed. However, it lacks hands and cannot manipulate things except with its mouth, and in this way is even more restricted than a bird. Yet there is language of sorts, with a great variety of sounds ranging from grunts to whistles, used as an intercom system within a school. The brain and the voice are there. The question is, what can the brain do and what does the language amount to? With such a pleasant fellow to deal with, if we cannot get to know him and understand his language, what chance have we of communicating with any creature, of comparable or greater intelligence, that may live on another planet? For here is no miniature computer, as is the brain of the bee, nor even the walnut-brained octopus, but the only creature on Earth who can match our own brain for size and the number of its cells. We are the johnnies-come-lately in this Earthly venture, and it is for us to make the attempt. If we fail here, we will fail everywhere else as well.

Point of No Return

ONE OF THE MORE PRESSING PROBLEMS facing mankind, in fact the most pressing of all problems if only we could forget our nuclear and ideological squabbling and look squarely at our present predicament, is the ominous threat of overpopulation. We are three billion people about to become six billion by the end of this century and, if the current rate of world increase continues for several more centuries, we will have literally no more than standing-room-only on the lands of the Earth. Planets look like places to plant the surplus, a solution that has already been proposed. In fact, to quote a well publicized rocket enthusiast who shall remain anonymous, there is

". . . no sense solving problems here on earth that may be altered, perhaps even wiped out, by future journeys through space. Our physical resources are severely limited and our population is constantly increasing. Isn't that one of the biggest problems we have, leading to poverty, war, and the Lord knows what? Well, if we turn the world into a vast emigration center, as I believe we can and will, then that old problem simply disappears. I see sending millions of adventurous pioneers out into space—opening up other planets as we once opened up the West. The universe is our oyster, and we're on our way."

That the world—now the world-universe of the astronomers—is our oyster, to be relished and ingested so that what was oyster becomes man, is merely an extension of a dominant human outlook stemming from the chronically bloody-minded northern European civilization which has now spread across the hemispheres. There are other outlooks, but Caesar's cry (I come, I see, I conquer) seems to be sweeping all before it.

Persons more seriously concerned about the future of mankind than those who are irresponsibly prepared to watch the home fire burn the house down while waiting for firemen in space ships to put it out look upon other planets either to rescue us from a more distant dilemma, or as fertile beds for human seed. A generation ago, after the near approach of Halley's comet, a possible catastrophic end to the Earth became at least a passing thought, and tales were told of mass emigration to Venus before the event occurred. A philosopher-teacher writes that space travel may some day spell the difference between life and death for mankind, when the Sun has changed to such an extent that life will be impossible on our own planet and we will skip from one to another throughout the galaxy to prolong the end beyond our time—playing a frantic game until there are no more games to play.

Two quite different questions are involved in these proposals: How far can we travel? and How much can we transport? although the one problem affects the other. The biologist Garrett Hardin has gone into the matter of exporting human surpluses to faraway places fairly thoroughly. This is not just a question of how far and how fast we can travel in space, but how effective such travel would be in relation to the rate of the continuing population increase at home. Modestly rather than optimistically, he selects the nearest star, 4.3 light years away, as the goal in space. At 19,000 miles per hour, roughly the speed at which our orbiting satellites travel, it would take 129,000 years to get there. Obviously such a slow speed would never do. On the basis of admittedly fantastic optimistic assumptions, however, it might be possible to make the transit in a mere 350 years, at an average speed of 7 million miles per hour, with 50 years required both for acceleration and deceleration.

Basing the cost of a rocket as low as $50 per pound and borrowing from our knowledge of atomic submarines for the ratio of man pounds to ship pounds, a suitable space ship would cost $3,000,000 per man traveling in it. Inasmuch as the population of the United States alone is increasing by more than three million people per year, the cost of shipping this many to other planets would be about $9,000 billion per year, which is roughly twenty times the gross national product. This is unrealistic enough. Yet if we extend the treatment, as is only logical, to the whole world population, which is increasing at the rate of about 125,000 per day, the shipping cost would be close to $400 billion simply to remove one day's increment. That is to say, the greater part of the total capital the American nation could set aside during a whole year would pay the cost of exporting only one day's growth of the world population. It doesn't make sense.

It makes less sense after the space ships cast off:

"Consider the human situation on board this astronomical *Mayflower*. For 350 years the population would have to live under conditions of complete sociological stasis, the like of which has never been known before. No births would be permitted, except to replace the dead (whose substance would, of course, have to be returned to the common stores). . . . The social organization would have to persist unchanged for ten generations' time. . . . It would be as if the space ship had to set sail, so to speak, under Captain John Smith and arrive at its goal under President Eisenhower, without the slightest change in ideas or ideals. . . . Those who seriously propose interstellar migration as a solution to overpopulation do so because they are unwilling to accept the necessity of controlling population numbers by means already at hand. They are unwilling to live, or to admit living, in a closed universe. Yet . . . that is precisely the sort of universe the interstellar migrants would be confined to, for some ten generations. Since the present annual rate of growth of the world's population is about 1.7 per cent, by the time the first ship arrived at its destination, the whole fleet of space ships en route would enclose a total population six times as large as that still present on the earth."

The whole business is full of absurdities. A continuous process of skimming either the cream or the scum of the earth's crop simply to keep the Earth itself in balance is fantastic in concept, impossible in terms of materials, effort, and expense, and represents a perpetual growing of surplus human material just to throw it out into space. The proposal is no better than using space for global radioactive garbage disposal—for which it may be well suited—and less humane in the end than the Nazi extermination camps. There is no outlet here, no landing, nor any return.

Travel in space must be for other reasons than easing the pressure of people here on Earth. Which leaves curiosity, scientific or otherwise, and the desire to plant our seed wherever it may grow. Is there anything else? Prestige, or greed under any other name? Whatever it is, the price will be high.

Putting aside all talk of population export and of cost and effort involved in sending even scientific probes into interstellar space, is there any possibility of sending manned space vehicles so far away, with or without some likelihood of returning? This leads us not only out of this world and out of this solar system, but almost out of mind. It takes us into the realm of mathematics and physics where a biologist should walk delicately and take the safer path of being a mere reporter. Accordingly, here is the gist of what Sebastian von Hoener, of the Astronomisches Rechen-Institut at Heidelberg, has to say on the general limits of space travel:

"The prime postulate in these estimates is a technology much more highly advanced than our present one. Accordingly, we completely neglect all technical problems, however serious they might be. Only such fundamental properties as time, acceleration, power, mass and energy are considered. The results are given in terms of the minimum travel times deriving from various assumptions. Furthermore, we calculate some basic requirements for reaching these travel times. . . . We need 5.4 kilograms of fuel to remove 1 kilogram of matter (from the earth against gravity), but the supply of fuel has to be accelerated too, and this again requires more fuel, and so on. Despite this difficulty of low fuel energy content, small payloads can still be removed, but with an

extremely low efficiency. The availability of more energetic fuels would not be of too much help. . . . With com-
bustion-powered rockets, even of many stages, we are
just able to leave the earth, but we cannot reach very
high velocities. . . . Nuclear reactors and all the equipment needed to give a strong ion thrust are so complicated and massive, as compared with the relatively simple
combustion equipment, that there is no hope at present
of reaching, with reactors, the value of P (power-mass
ratio) already attained with combustion rockets. . . . We
should assume that life and intelligence will have developed, with the same speed as on earth, wherever the
proper surroundings and the needed time have been provided. From our present limited data, we judge this
might have been the case on planets of about 6 per cent
of all stars. The nearest ten such stars are at an average
distance from us of about 5.6 parsec (1 parsec $= 3.09 \times$
$10^{13} km = 3.26$ light years). . . . With respect to interstellar space travel we must clearly separate two questions:
(*i*) We may want to know what the possibilities are for
our future interstellar travel. In this case we are interested in locating *any* kind of intelligent life, and the distance we are required to reach is

5.6 parsec ($= 18.6$ light-years);

(*ii*) We may examine the possibility of other beings visiting us. In this case the other civilization must be a *technical* one, and for the calculations that follow we will
use, for the above-mentioned distance to be covered by
these other beings,

250 parsec ($= 820$ light-years).

"In order to visualize these astronomical distances, I
will describe them with a model to scale 1:180 billion.

The earth, then, is a tiny grain of desert sand, just visible to the naked eye, orbiting around its sun, which is now a cherrystone a little less than 3 feet away. Within approximately the same distance, some few feet, lies the goal of our present space travel: the other planets of our solar system, such as Mars and Venus. But the nearest star, Proxima Centauri, is another cherrystone 140 miles away; and the next stars with habitable planets, where we might look for intelligent life, are to be expected at a distance of 610 miles. The next technical civilizations, however, will be at a distance as great as the circumference of the earth. Just for fun one may add the distance to the Andromeda nebula, the next stellar system comparable to our own galaxy: in our model it is as far away as, in reality, the sun is from the earth. The most distant galaxies seen by astronomers with their best telescopes are 2,000 times as far away, and here even our model fails to help us.

"One thing is now clear: in order to cover interstellar distances within reasonable times we ought to fly as close as possible to the velocity of light, the utmost limit of any velocity, according to the theory of relativity (and in accordance with all experiments with high-velocity particles). But as we approach the velocity of light, the formulas of normal physics must be replaced by those of relativity theory.

"This might be of some help, because one of the most striking statements of relativity theory is that time itself is not an absolute property but is shortened for systems approaching the velocity of light. If, for example, we are to move out and back a distance of 800 light-years, then people remaining on earth will have to wait at least 1,600 years for the return of the rocket. But if the speed of the rocket closely approaches the velocity of light, then the flow of time for this rocket and its crew becomes different from that on earth, and one may expect that the crew members will have to spend only a few years, perhaps, of their own lifetimes between start and return.

"Having seen . . . that the energy per mass of fuel is one of the most important considerations in space travel, we now ask for the most energetic fuels. The utmost possible limit is set by one of the fundamental laws of relativity: $E = mc^2$ which gives the energy E obtained by complete annihilation of matter of mass m. . . . Complete annihilation takes place only if matter and antimatter are brought together: when a proton combines with an antiproton, electron combines with positron, and so on. But the world we live in consists of matter only, and to store a large amount of antimatter with equipment consisting of matter seems quite impossible, from all we know. We thus have to look for another source of energy. . . . The only fuel used at present for space travel releases energy by chemical reactions. . . . If we learn to use uranium reactors instead, the energy-mass ratio will be increased by a factor of 5.6 million. If ever it becomes possible to use the fusion of hydrogen into helium as a power source for space travel, one would gain another factor of 10; and if complete annihilation were practicable, a further factor of 140 would be gained.

"Thus equipped with an understanding of nuclear fuel, if not with the real thing, and with relativistic formulas, we proceed with estimating the general limits of future space travel. . . . As a first step we neglect even the requirements of energy and power. The only limitation then remaining will be the maximum amount of acceleration which a crew can stand. . . . It seems likely that, *over a long trip*, any crew will stand only about as much acceleration as its members are used to experiencing on their home planet. . . . The shortest travel time for a given distance will result if we accelerate with 1g half of the way and then decelerate with 1g over the second half of the trip, returning in the same way. . . . The relativistic time dilatation yields an effective gain only if the crew members spend more than 10 years of their lives on the voyage. The further increase, however, is a very steep one (exponential); if the crew members spent 30 years of their lives on the voyage they would be able to fly to the Orion nebula and back, and 3,000 years would have elapsed on earth between their departure and their return. . . ." With these results, many readers may already have lost hope of future interstellar space travel; others still may be optimistic.

"So far we have neglected payloads and fuel. . . . As an example we start with a 'small' space ship of 10-ton payload, and we add another 10 tons for power plant plus emitters. If we want to reach a velocity within 2 per cent of that of light (with a dilatation factor of 5), we need a mass ratio of $M = 10$ . . . and the total mass of the rocket will be 200 tons. . . . In order to get an acceleration of $b = 1g$, we would need a power output of 600 million megawatts. Thus, we would need 40 million annihilation power plants of 15 megawatts each, plus 6 billion transmitting stations of 100 kilowatts each, altogether having no more mass than 10 tons, in order to approach the velocity of light to within 2 per cent within 2.3 years of the crew's time. . . . Or . . . if one wants to get an acceleration of, say, $b = 100g$, in order to take full advantage of a deep-frozen crew, then 100 times the equipment mentioned . . . must not total more than 10 tons; this means that power plants plus transmitters should have an output of 6,000 megawatts per gram. . . . There is no way of avoiding these demands, and definitely no hope of fulfilling them."

With all this talk about relative time perhaps the biologist should intrude again, although only to add more fuel to this funeral pyre. The physicist's concept of the relative change in time as the velocity of light is approached has meaning in the mathematico-physical world alone. Any organism that left the neighborhood of the Earth and returned to it could not avoid aging to the extent of the Earthly time it had been away, unless fast-frozen or desiccated in some way that no sane human would tolerate. Whether human or not, a living thing lives in local time wherever it may be, whatever the speed at which its vehicle travels through space. To us the Earth is stationary in spite of its headlong passage together with the solar system as a whole through interstellar space, not to mention its slower movement around the Sun. The fact remains that the matter that makes up the organism does not move significantly, either as an organized whole or as mere substance, relative to the space immediately surrounding it, and for an organism to be itself it will age in its accustomed way, not according to the relativity of time of a mathematical equation, but according to the beating of its heart and the aging of its cells. This kind of time is where you are, and has no relation to how fast you are speeding through nothing.

The biologist, then, is of the same mind as the atomic physicist and can say with von Hoener—"This is, at present, all we can do, and the final conclusion as to the feasibility of such ventures is up to the reader. The requirements, however, have turned out to be such extreme ones that I, personally, draw this conclusion: space travel, even in the most distant future, will be confined completely to our own planetary system, and a similar conclusion will hold for any other civilization, no matter how advanced it will be. The only means of communication between different civilizations thus seems to be electromagnetic signals."

So—we seem to be back where we started. Except for the belief that there are life-supporting planets orbiting around myriads of more or less genial suns scattered throughout the Milky Way galaxy, and equally throughout the billions of generally similar galaxies distributed through the visible and invisible universe. And a last, lean hope that by listening intently in the dark we may possibly hear some sort of patterned pulse in radio noise reaching us from the great outer emptiness. Perhaps, too, we can send radio signals which will reach a receptive ear. However small the chance that something will be heard, if we don't listen or don't send there is no chance at all, either way.

Listening and sending both assume far more than the presence of planets inhabited by intelligent life, within range. They also assume that any such intelligent life has evolved a technological society at least as good as and presumably much better than our own. Even with this assumption, we have to consider the possibility that our distant neighbors may reckon our solar system to be too young for their attention. We are, after all, cosmically speaking, still damp from birth. One wag has suggested that if we do succeed in butting in on the galactic party line, the first message we decode will be 'hang up, you idiot!'

However this may be, the only means of establishing contact available to us is some form of electromagnetic radiation. At least it is a great advance over some early proposals for interplanetary signaling. One was that great ditches be dug in the Sahara desert, filled with water, and covered with burning kerosene for several hours each night, in the hope that Martians would observe them. Now it is all electronics. The radiowave chosen both for listening and sending is the 21-centimeter wavelength, which is that radiated by interstellar hydrogen. It is of such great interest to astronomers that it is the one wavelength that commercial interests have so far been prevented from commandeering. This wavelength is so significant that intelligent technological beings elsewhere are likely to have selected it for their own intragalactic broadcasting. The most difficult problem in interstellar communication is the technical one of conveying a signal over vast distances so that it will still be meaningful at the far end in spite of being immensely weakened. Using the hydrogen band and a high antenna, however, it may be possible to signal out to a range of nearly 1,000 light-years, more than far enough to take in the whole of our galaxy and its satellite galaxies, the Clouds of Magellan, but not the next true galaxy, Andromeda.

Suppose we start sending, when can we expect a response? To send a message to the far side of our galaxy, for instance, more than 100,000 years would pass before a reply, if any, could be received, which is about as long as human beings have been on Earth in their present form, and twenty times longer than the entire history of human civilization. Even a message to Betelgeuse or Rigel, which are among our nearest neighbors and within the range we should reach if we are to have a chance of finding a technological society, would take several hundred years to get there, and a reply would take just as long to come back. By the time it came through, no one on Earth would remember what had been said in the first place, judging from the changing state of our own society during the last two centuries.

Whether or not we decide to send our own signals into space, the listening has already begun. If interstellar signaling has any merit, it must be because other living communities are already practicing it. There is no point in having a telephone all by yourself. And we are at such a moment in time ourselves that it is unreasonable to assume no one has lifted a receiver before us. If messages there are, they must have been going on for ages past, between transmitters far more advanced than ourselves. It is for us to listen and, if possible, to recognize them if they are there.

Radio telescopes have already been listening for possible signals from the nearest stars, at the U.S. National Radio Astronomy Observatory in West Virginia, so far without success, although the marginal sensitivity of the receiving apparatus could be responsible. If a message should get through, however, what would it be like? Dr. Frank Drake, of this Observatory, has invented an example of the sort of message which might have arrived from outside the solar system, consisting of 551 zeros and ones. It appeared in a publication having the enchanting title "Periodic Communications of the Order of the Dolphins." See if you can decipher it. The key lies in the number itself. (The number 551 is product of two prime numbers only, 29 × 19. Make two rectangles, one consisting of 29 rows of 19 spaces, and the other of 19 rows of 29 spaces. Fill in each space corresponding to a figure 1, and leave blank the spaces corresponding to zeros. One completed rectangle will tell you something; the other will not.)

111100001010010000110010000000010000010100
100000110010110011110000011000011010000000
001000001000010000100010101000010000000000
000000000010001000000000010110000000000000
000000010001110110101101010000000000000000
000010010000111010101010000000000101010101
000000000111010101011101011000000001000000
000000000001000000000000010001001111111000
001110100000101100000111000000001000000000
100000000100000001111100000010110001011110
100000001100101111101011111100010011111001
000000000001111100000010110001111111100000
100000110000011000010000100000001100001
001000111100101111

Example of a Message That Might Be
Received from Another Civilization in Space

If nothing ever comes through, what then? Perhaps all we can say is that it was fun while it lasted, and recognize the fact of our isolation—what the English writer C. S. Lewis has called God's Quarantine Regulations. Yet when all is done we are still traveling through space as fast as anyone, and on as good a space ship as creation has provided. In the words of J. Donald Adams of *The New York Times:*

"When will man get it through his head that his choice of a celestial speck to inhabit was a very shrewd one, and that in spite of the mayhem he has committed upon his native Earth, it remains the one hospitable world he is likely to encounter. Let him, then, redouble his efforts to improve it, instead of horsing around beyond its stratosphere."

Earth as a Space Ship

AN ULTIMATE END awaits any sun and planet, and ours will not be excepted. Yet there are still several billion years of future for the descendants of at least some of the inhabitants of the Earth. To round things off a little, we can say that the present time is close to five billion years from the beginning and something like five billion from the end. Five billion is of course a short way of saying it. In terms a little more readily appreciated, when we consider how much human history has been encompassed in the last thousand years, a future which extends through five thousand thousand thousands of years is, to all effect, eternity. In this light, our particular human problem seems less a question of getting to other planets than of staying on this one. Who will inherit the Earth? There is no doubt that the Earth will continue its course through time and space, complete with a living freight, in spite of anything we may do. But will we ourselves remain on board as passengers? And if we do manage to hang on, what eventually will be our nature, appearance, and behavior?

From the first wetness to the present explosiveness, Sun

and Earth, not to mention the other planets, have been whirling along through space in happy concert, each planet circling the Sun in its own good time. For four to five billion years the Sun has spun on its own axis some sixty billion times. In their own way the solar revolutions are the heartbeat of the solar system, the measure of time and life for all attendant planets whether or not they have a dance of life of their own. Yet the galaxy as a whole has made its spiral turn less than twenty times in the same eternal period, and clearly has a destiny, or at least a lifetime, far exceeding that of any single star. Sun, planets, and living freight have already journeyed through enough of both space and time to more than satisfy any urge to travel for travel's sake alone—riding the rim of the galactic wheel ten million miles a day ever since time began on Earth. We travel a superhighway that passes everything by but has no destination. The Earth, in fact and not merely in fancy, is a space ship traveling alongside a star. We keep our course at the proper distance alongside a powerful, life-sustaining convoy, with our own protective magnetic and atmospheric envelopes. This is our place and it is where we belong, with adventure enough if we have but the wits to know it. Make no mistake, the self-perpetuating life of this pirouetting planet has already had an amazing past, and is rushing into the future at a headlong pace.

To travel through space, if it is to mean anything at all, is to travel through time. Here is the real excitement, for whereas traveling through nothing arrives at nothing, journeying through time is to move in the fourth dimension. We and all that are about us are creatures or creations of time, not space. Time past, the eternal present, and time future. This is what we are concerned with. Wherever the Earth has wandered, wherever it will go, makes little difference. The main event, from our point of view, is the

Earth itself in its process of flowering—an almost ever-lasting present that has endured and will endure for time out of mind. Our special human privilege is to encompass it, as one would appreciate and retain an unfinished symphony, not perfectly, but as best we can.

A symphony, however, not only exists in time. It is or-chestrated. So with life. All Earthly life is one, both as an integrated whole flourishing at the moment, and as one that has progressed in concert from the start. The first movements were slow and quiet and are difficult to recall. Later movements became more striking. The present is strident. And through it all there is an ever-accelerating pace.

Here are the real events of our universe, at least so far as we are concerned, then, now, and hereafter. At a great rate, things have been happening and are obviously going to happen. We urgently need to know where we have come from, where we are, and where we are going. Even if no destination can be seen, at least we can look at our wake and get a sense of direction. As the world has changed, so have we and all our companions in life. This particular moment in time, which is the present of our brief, individ-ual lives, is no place at all. We ride the tiger, carried for-ward by cosmic energy we cannot contain.

The only worlds, other than the here and now, that we have any real prospect of looking into are the worlds of the past that our various ancestors and their respective con-temporary companions have inhabited during the last sev-eral hundred million years on Earth. Before that even the local pageant becomes enveloped in a thick haze, with mere glimmerings of ghostly happenings taking place in a time that seems diluted and interminable. Yet back in those faint drawn-out beginnings, the course to the pres-ent became set. This is also the course to the future, for the massive complexity of this moving event called evolution is such that no puny human efforts are going to thwart it or give it an entirely new direction. We can take the wheel if we choose, and gain the illusion of being in control, and may even succeed in rocking the boat, but when all is said and done we still are passengers, and at that are merely one class of a motley crowd. It behooves us to act accordingly. We have come a long way, and we have a long, long way to go.

Look backward for a moment at those worlds from which we have come. From the very beginning and throughout about half of the whole of lapsed time on Earth, life was formless except at a microscopic and molecular level. During one or two thousand million years, or about one million times the duration of the Christian era, the organic chemical complexities of the Earth's watery envelope evolved into discrete cells which were the foundation of all life to come. Such was the first world of this planet, and cells were the primary creation, each an organism in itself. There is no unit of life less than the cell, and all else depends upon it. Its structure and performance are amazing, and its full nature still eludes us. Though the individual scale is small, the creative event was probably of planetary extent. We should not feel too surprised that as much time went into the creation and perfection of the units of life as has since gone into using them to make bigger and ever more elaborate organisms.

The second world of our forebeing followed imperceptibly on the first, and for another thousand million years or so. Cell-organisms with the process and apparatus for intensive photosynthesis became dominant in the waters and set free so much oxygen that the atmosphere became more or less what it is today. And with this abundance of oxygen available, the animal world progressively took on a more animated look. Long before the thousand millennia were over, judging by the aftermath, the animal kingdom was present, at least in all its main shoots and in multicellular forms. Yet all life remained aquatic.

With more than three-quarters of lapsed time already gone, the world of animals took on a more tangible and spectacular look. The arena, to begin with, was still exclusively aquatic and mainly marine. The great continental areas to be were mostly submerged platforms covered by shallow seas. For two or three hundred million years, a long period but only one tenth of the time that had gone before, the seas teemed with molluscs, giant and otherwise, and with crustaceans, sea stars, and coral. Fish became truly fish in the fresh waters, sending their quota to the seas in the shape of sharks and other kinds. This era, from the Cambrian to the Devonian, is fully substantiated in fossiliferous form and, compared with all that had gone before, is a world apparent in relatively sharp focus. And, with some later additions from more terrestrial regions, this marine world has continued to the present, basically unchanged although forever changing in lesser ways.

Shallow continental seas went hand in hand with emergent continental land sodden with draining rains, particularly through the Devonian period and its successor, the Carboniferous. While the drama of the shallow and the high seas intensified with passing time, a transient semi-terrestrial world evolved partaking of meandering freshwater ways, swamps, and air so moist an aquatic creature hardly knew whether it was coming or going. This was the world of uplifting plants, particularly tree ferns and all that went to the making of coal. Scuttling insects took shape on the damp terrain and, as adventurous, air-breathing fish, with fins half legs already, emerged from the greater wetness to feed upon them, they grew wings and flew away. Humid fern-like forests, giant dragonflies and cockroaches, and old four-legs himself, scrambling about in amphibious earnestness between swamp and soggy land, made up a world of comparatively short duration.

Then, as the Earth took breath and the continental plains rose slowly, water drained faster to the sea. Conifers grew where none had been, and scaly reptiles, with faster legs, with large, white-shelled eggs to be laid on land, became the scenery and the players. And for a hundred million years—a hundred thousand thousand years—so small a part of the total time but so long an act in reality, this was the world. A somber, majestic, thundering, small-brained reptilian world without a flower to speak of. But an inventive world for all that, with flying reptiles great and small, and giant fishlike lizards mastering the seas. Yet it came to an end.

Time continues, with but another hundred million years to go before we find ourselves in its crest. A new world grew where the old had ceased to flourish—no doubt imperceptibly at the time but rather suddenly in retrospect. Plants and insects bloomed together, to give flowers of all shapes and colors, and butterflies, bees, and moths in addition to beetles. Trees became manifold and decidu-ous, and birds took over mastery of the air in a renewed pursuit of insects. And with reptiles no longer in their glory the small, hairy, live-birthing mammals came out of their long seclusion and grew into the community of horses, antelopes, apes, elephants, bears, bats, cats, seals, whales, and all the rest we are familiar with, including many that flourished in their time but failed to reach the present. A world of mammals, birds, insects, flowers, trees and grasses—our world, if you like—came into being and, in battered shape, is with us yet.

As each world succeeded another, the drama intensified, quickened, and the players became more colorful and numerous. The Age of Reptiles gave way to that of mammals. Then man appeared and a new world began, the end of which is not in sight.

This last world is recent, of the order of a million years. It may have been foreshadowed, but the change from the old to the new came suddenly with the beginning of the Ice Age. Great glacial sheets spread southward from near the Pole, the tropics narrowed, and climatically the Earth was in tumult, with the great cold coming and going throughout at least half-a-million years. Glacial and interglacial periods have alternated with one another, except in tropical regions where the alternation has been between wetter and drier respectively. Just now we seem to be about midway through one of the milder phases.

This is the world of man, and the twilight of most of the larger mammals that had it mainly to themselves for so long a time. A million years ago there was no ice and nothing human except some slight, scampering, stone-throwing, cave-sheltering bipeds maintaining a precarious existence. It took the shattering impact of ice and cold on the dominant mammalian fauna, and the discovery of fire by the little sprinters or their descendants, to set man on the road to ascendancy. And with fire of one kind or another he has continued what the ice began. The Age of Mammals is as clearly over now as the Age of Reptiles was when mammals hesitantly took over the field. Yet this age of man and ice and fire has lasted far less than one thousandth of living time.

As a dominant creature, savage as well as sophisticated, the human kind has made itself felt for no more than thirty thousand years or so, with his civilizations but a fraction of that. This is no time at all on the evolutionary scale, and it is in this moment of awakening that we are discovering ourselves and the universe about us. It is natural enough to look at the stars and to think of jumping the space between us and them as though to the branch of another tree. It is an entertaining distraction and probably a harmless, if expensive, escapade. The danger is that we look away too long from the task at hand, which is to keep our equilibrium in time and space aboard the planet that bears us. Above all, we need a clearer view of what is going on, for we are moving now at a giddy pace and know not what lies ahead.

To begin with, we are barely beginning to understand what sort of planet it is that we inhabit. The Earth is no mere ball of spinning matter. What is happening beneath our feet may signify more than anything the other planets may have to say. Is there truly a liquid metallic core streaming about a solid metallic center, responsible for the existence and the shifting of the Earth's magnetic field? How mobile is the immensely thick mantle? Do convection currents in its stony substance cause the continental masses in the crust to slide about? Is the whole Atlantic Ocean a fairly recent rifting-apart of a continental mass? Does the spin of the Earth cause heavy metals to sink toward the center, and is water forever being squeezed through the crust by the same centrifugal force, so that oceans deepen with time? What pushes up mountain ranges, and what initiates ice ages at long intervals and the fluctuations within them? This is the Earth we have to come to terms with, which has produced us, and where our future lies.

It is a most lively planet, physically and organically. All life, including us whether we like it or not, is driven remorselessly through change and time by the energy of the

Sun forever entering the system. This is the power that drives our space ship, with the Earth's spinning core as a gyroscope and clock. And as in any hypothetical space ship, the voyage through space and eternity is self-contained— there is no going back for fresh supplies or new life to replace the old. Life on any space ship that journeys for any truly considerable length of time can persist only so long as all waste and the dead are returned to the living system as a whole. On a man-made space ship this necessity raises not so much insoluble problems as intolerable solutions. On the Earth the solutions are just as inevitable, but they are the conditions of our individual and collective existence and we accept them, gracefully or otherwise, because we have no choice.

Two facts of life stand out. The total productivity of the Earth is definite, not unlimited. Just so much life of all kinds together can exist at one time, the total quantity depending less on the availability and abundance of solar energy and the principal elements constituting all living matter, such as carbon, hydrogen, oxygen and nitrogen, than on equally essential elements required in smaller quantity but relatively scarce at the surface of the planet, such as phosphorus, almost literally the spark of life.

The other is that life exists only as individual organisms all of which, as individuals, have a passing existence, ranging from the twenty minutes of a bacterium to the eighty years of a man. Life may be almost immortal, but lives are not. It follows that lives must go on succeeding lives for as long as time lasts, and that the same matter must be used over and over again, and to the very limit. By the same token, our common practice of putting the human dead out of circulation in leaden caskets is a biological misdemeanor which could well become a deadly sin.

In any case, life is constrained by these parameters. The forms may change as the generations flick by, but the aggregate remains the same. If there should be more of one kind there will be less of others. If some live longer lives, it will in some way be at the expense of numbers. The more human beings there are, sustained by cattle and corn, so much less is left for everything else. And so it goes. We have produced a technological society, beginning about ten thousand years ago and now enveloping the whole planet, with everything grist to its mill. Three billion humans now, six billion by the end of the century, goodness knows how many thereafter, all gobbling up the substance of the Earth, all living out the full span of the individual human life—what sort of world will it be? What sort of world could it be? Do we breed for the maximum number of spindle-legged, chronically hungry, pot-bellied morons, or for some far smaller number of vigorous, creative humans that justify all of the long past that has gone into the making? If man does not live by bread alone, what else does he need—of beauty, wildness, thought and action? If there are too many of us, and mostly too old at that, what else can there be? Before we go anywhere at all we must trim the ship, by hook or by crook bringing our numbers and our habits into keeping with the voyage. For this storm is already upon us.

When the Earth, with all its rich variety of life and its human cargo, is in balance again, where do we go, if anywhere? In the short run we make the best of what we are and where we are—literally so. That should be occupation and destiny enough for a good many thousand years. In the longer run we can evolve biologically, with our own hand at the helm if you like, into something more human than we already are, for what other road is possible or desirable? We have come a short way from the ape and there is a long way to go, with time no man can see. Or failing all this, we can fade from the scene and what is left of life will eventually make another good show, for there will be worlds aplenty here on Earth before Earthly time runs out.

Further Reading

You and the Universe, by N. J. Berrill; Dodd, Mead and Company.

Frontiers of Astronomy, by Fred Hoyle; Harper and Row.

Planets, Stars and Galaxies, by S. I. Inglis; John Wiley and Sons.

Of Stars and Men, by Harlow Shapley; Beacon Press, Inc.

The Meaning of Evolution, by G. G. Simpson; Yale University Press (and Mentor).

Life of the Past, by G. G. Simpson; Yale University Press.

The Planet Mars, by G. de Vaucouleurs; Faber and Faber.

Man and His Future, by G. Wolstenholme (ed.); Little, Brown and Company.

INDEX

Index

Abelson, Dr. Philip, 33
Adams, J. Donald, 221
Aesop, 164
Age of Mammals, 228
Age of Reptiles, 86, 100, 109
albedo, the, 10
algae, 12, 58
Alphonsus, 23
amino acids, 69
ammonia, 12, 43, 67, 74 ff.
Amoeba, 7
Andromeda, 214, 219
angular momentum, 78
ants, 160–61
Apt, the, 83–84, 86
asteroids, 46, 70–71, 75
astronauts, 42, 45
Astronomisches Rechen-Institut,
    212
Atlantic Ocean, 113, 229

Back to Methuselah, 170
bacteria, 58, 66
    capture of Martian, 59
    contamination of space by, 61

bathyscaphe, 107
bees, 167
    caste system of, 160
    communication between, 197–
    98
"Before Eden," 5
Betelgeuse, 219
bilateral symmetry, 124, 126–
    27
biparental reassortment, 184,
    185
birds, 102 ff., 167
Blake, William, 128
body temperature, 148
Brahe, Tycho, 15, 56
Bulletin of the American Insti-
    tute of Biological Sciences,
    35
Burroughs, Edgar Rice, 82, 83

Cambrian period, the, 226
Canary Islands, the, 113
carbohydrates, 67, 69
carbon, 67, 75, 81, 94
carbon dioxide, 12, 13, 43, 67, 75

carbon monoxide, 67
Catholic Church, 15
centipede, 141, 145
cephalopod molluscs, 142–43
Ceres, 71
Chesterton, G. K., 201
chitin, 141
chlorophyll, 123
Clarke, Arthur, 5
Clouds of Magellan, 219
communication, 193 ff.
  insect, 195, 196
  interplanetary, 218
  with the porpoise, 194, 195,
    203 ff.
Copernicus, 56, 59
cosmic rays, 41, 45
Cousteau, Jacques, 112, 113, 114,
  194, 204
craters of the Moon, 24

Dampier, William, 48
Daphnia, 156, 157
Darwin, Charles, 17, 23, 35, 59
Darwin, George, 23
deep-sea scattering layer, 115,
  116
Deimos, 51
"De Profundis," 109
Devonian period, the, 226
double stars, 180, 188 ff.
Drake, Dr. Frank, 220

Earth, 66, 166, 229 ff.
  atmosphere of, 67, 69
  effect of solar gravity on, 23
  formation of, 23, 64
  gravitational pull of the Moon
    on, 16, 22

Earth *(cont.)*
  internal temperature of, 27
  orbit of, 65
  origin of water on, 25
  rotation of, 166 ff.
echinoderms, 142
Echo I, 30
echo-location, 206
eggs, 152, 155–56
elephant bird, 171
elephants, 99, 100
Elizabeth I, 15
environmental pressure, 184
epicontinental seas, 117–18
evolution, 88 ff., 183 ff., 225 ff.
  and gravity, 94 ff.
  and horses, 98–99
  and man, 38 ff.
exobiology, 2, 35, 36, 60
eyes, 133 ff.
eye-hand brain, 39
eye-spots, 131

fatty acids, 69
firefly, 196
fireworms, 166
fish, 186, 194–95
flying saucers, 4
Forel, August, 167
fossils, 88, 186
frogs, 196
From Fish to Philosopher, 141

galaxies, 79
Galileo, 15, 25, 48, 51, 56, 72,
  73
Geiger counter, 45
glaciers, 28

gravity, 91 ff.
  and living things, 94 ff.
  and evolution, 98 ff.
gravity-sensitive organs, 131–32
Great Red Spot, 71, 73
Gulliver's Travels, 50

Haldane, J. B. S., 128
Hall, Asaph, 51
Halley's comet, 209
Hardin, Garrett, 210
Hellas, 55
hemoglobin, 125
hermaphrodites, 153, 155
Hokusai, 194, 202
horses, 98–99
horseshoe crab, 186
hydrocarbons, 1, 10, 11
hydrogen, 64, 67, 75, 94
hydrogen band, 219

Ice Age, 186, 228
ichthyosaurs, 109
insects, 102 ff., 145 ff., 160 ff.
  and gravity, 102
  communication among, 195–96
  physical characteristics of,
    145 ff.
  societies of, 160 ff.
intelligence, 193, 194, 199
internal clock, 167, 168
interplanetary communication,
    218

jellyfish, 9, 65, 126–27, 151
Jet Propulsion Laboratory, 1
Jungfrau, 55
Jupiter, 1, 64, 70, 71, 75, 76, 164
  atmosphere of, 71–72
  gravity of, 72, 92, 93, 96

Jupiter (*cont.*)
  moons of, 51, 72, 73
  orbit of, 65
  rotation of, 71, 78

Kepler, John, 15 ff., 48, 56, 60,
    70, 182
keratin, 140
kidneys, 141

legs, 100, 143 ff.
Leinster, Murray, 109
Lewis, C. S., 221
lichens, 8, 9, 58, 122
life
  duration of, 163 ff., 174–75
  extraterrestrial, 79
  origin of, 29, 66 ff.
  requirements for, 74
light-sensitive organs, 131
living fossils, 186
locomotion, 144 ff.
  of insects, 145–57
  of vertebrates, 146
London, Jack, 126
longevity, 163 ff., 174–75
Lowell, Dr. Percival, 52
luminosity, 179–80
Lutheran Church, 15

Madeira, 113
magnetic fields, 23, 45, 229
man
  and gravity, 95
  effects of space on, 46
  evolution of, 38 ff., 89
  physical characteristics of, in
    space, 33 ff., 41, 42
Man and Superman, 153
marine life, 107 ff.

Mariner I, 1n.
Mariner II, 1
Mars, 1, 42, 49 ff., 64, 66, 75, 164
    atmosphere of, 54
    canals on, 51–52
    exploration of, 46, 59–60
    moons of, 49, 51
    orbit of, 53, 65
    polar caps of, 54
    temperature on, 53
    vegetation on, 54–55, 56, 58
    water on, 55–56
median eye, 134
memory, 170
mental telepathy, 193
Mercury, 1, 11, 64
    distance from Sun of, 14
    effect of solar gravity on, 23
    orbit of, 65
    possibility of life on, 57
    rotation of, 23
meteorites, 24, 46, 81
meteoritic dust, 29
meteors, 28
methane, 67
Milky Way, 16, 79, 166
millipede, 141, 144–45
Moon, the, 13 ff.
    cost of trip to, 32–33
    formation of, 23
    gravitational pull of, 27
    internal temperature of, 27
    magnetic field of, 23
    manned exploration of, 32
    origin of craters on, 24
    rotation of, 22
    surface of, 28
    water on, 185
mutations, 184–85

National Aeronautics and Space
    Administration (NASA), 30,
    35, 37, 47
natural selection, 125, 184
Neptune, 64
    orbit of, 65
    temperature of, 73
New York Times, The, 221
*New Voyage Round the World,
    A,* 48
nitrogen, 12, 54, 75
North Africa, 114
nuclear war, 185

oceans, 106 ff.
octopus, 142–43, 195, 199
Origin of Species, 17
overpopulation, 208 ff.
oxygen, 16, 43, 54, 67, 75, 94,
    107, 225
oysters, 122
ozone, 44, 69

Pacific Ocean, 23
Pantheon, the, 1
parthenogenesis, 156–57
Phobos, 51
phosphorus, 8, 60
photosynthesis, 67, 69
Plant Men of Barsoom, 84 ff.
plants, 121 ff.
Pluto, 64
polygamy, 158
Pope, Alexander, 80
porpoises, 194, 195, 203 ff.
Porquerollas, 114
preadaptation, 140
Priestley, Joseph, 16
protein, 65
protobiochemistry, 35

protoplanets, 64, 66, 78
protoplasm, 65, 70, 74–75
Proxima Centauri, 214
pterosaurs, 147
Ptolemaic universe, 15

radial symmetry, 124, 126–27
radiation
    atomic, 185
    cosmic, 29, 45
    solar, 16, 29, 41, 44, 69, 185
radioactive decay, 27
radiowave studies, 28
Ranger series, 1n.
red giant, 179
reproduction, 87, 150 ff.
reptiles, 186
Reynolds, Orr, 47
Rigel, 219
Roc, the, 171
Rothstein, Jerome, 202
royal jelly, 160

Salvagem Grande, 113, 114
Sargasso Sea, 108
Saturn, 1, 64, 73
    orbit of, 65
scallops, 93, 134
Schiaparelli, Giovanni, 51
Science, 33
sea anemone, 126, 127
sea pens, 108, 117
sea serpent, 109
sea squirts, 117
Selenite, 82
sensory organs, 129, 131 ff., 136
sex, 150 ff.
sex cells, 151–52, 155
Shackleton expedition, 61
shape and gravity, 94 ff.

Shaw, George Bernard, 122, 153, 170, 171, 172, 173
shrimp, 116, 153–54
sight, 132, 135
Silent World, The, 194
simple eye, 132
Sirius, 120
Sith, the, 84, 86
size and gravity, 96 ff.
sleep, 200
smell, 195
Smith, Homer, 141
solar flares, 45
solar radiation, 16, 29, 41, 44, 69, 185
solar sailing, 30–31
solar system, 63–64, 76 ff., 181
sonar, 206
space
    asteroids in, 45–46
    contamination of, 61–62
    food problems in, 47
    man in, 33 ff., 41, 42
    radiation in, 29, 45
space biology, *see* exobiology
space ships, 230
    sterilization of, 61
space travel, 41 ff., 209 ff.
    food problems during, 47
    hazards of, 44 ff.
    psychological problems of, 46
sperm, 152, 155
spiders, 135
sponges, 117, 123–24, 125
spores, 29–30
squid, 108–09, 116, 142, 194, 195
starfish, 108, 117, 142
stars, 78, 179
subsurface glaciers, 28

Sun, the, 64, 178, 179, 223
    gravitational effect of, 23
    rotation of, 78
Swift, Jonathan, 48, 50
symbiosis, 43
symmetry, 124, 126–27

taste, 195, 199 ff.
teeth, 175
telepathy, 193
termites, 161
time, 163 ff.
touch, 195, 199 ff.
Tycho, 19

ultraviolet, 44, 69
United States National Radio
    Astronomy Observatory, 220
University of Chicago, 67
Uranus, 64, 73
Urey, H. E., 67

Van Allen belts, 45
Vanguard, 30
vegetative reproduction, 151
Venus, 1, 64, 65, 107, 164
    atmosphere of, 2, 11 ff.

Venus (*cont.*)
    effect of solar gravity on, 23
    magnetic field of, 23
    orbit of, 23
    possibility of life on, 4 ff., 10
    rotation of, 23
    surface of, 2
    temperature of, 10
    water on, 10–11, 12
Verne, Jules, 17, 19, 23, 24, 80,
    83
Von Braun, Dr. Wernher, 32
Von Hoener, Sebastian, 212, 217

War of the Worlds, The, 82
water, 9, 25, 65, 75, 107
water vapor, 54, 67
waterflea, 156, 157
Weaver, Dr. Warren, 32
Wells, H. G., 82, 83, 92
whales, 137
Wheeler, William Morton, 161
wings, 147
World War II, 167

X-rays, 45

Year of the Quiet Sun, 45